ELVIS PRESLEY
THE 50 GREATE

Wise Publications
London/New York/Sydney/Paris/Copenhagen/Madrid/Tokyo

Exclusive distributors:
Music Sales Limited
14/15 Berners Street,
London W1T 3LJ, England.
Music Sales Pty Limited
20 Resolution Drive,
Caringbah, NSW 2229,
Australia.

Order No.AM969419
ISBN 0-7119-8755-6

Music arranged by Rikky Rooksby
Music processed by The Pitts

Photographs courtesy of Rex Features London

Printed in the United Kingdom by
Caligraving Limited, Thetford, Norfolk.

Your Guarantee of Quality
As publishers, we strive to produce every book to the highest commercial standards. The book has been carefully designed to minimise awkward page turns and to make playing from it a real pleasure. Particular care has been given to specifying acid-free, neutral-sized paper made from pulps which have not been elemental chlorine bleached. This pulp is from farmed sustainable forests and was produced with special regard for the environment. Throughout, the printing and binding have been planned to ensure a sturdy, attractive publication which should give years of enjoyment. If your copy fails to meet our high standards, please inform us and we will gladly replace it.

www.musicsales.com

Relative Tuning

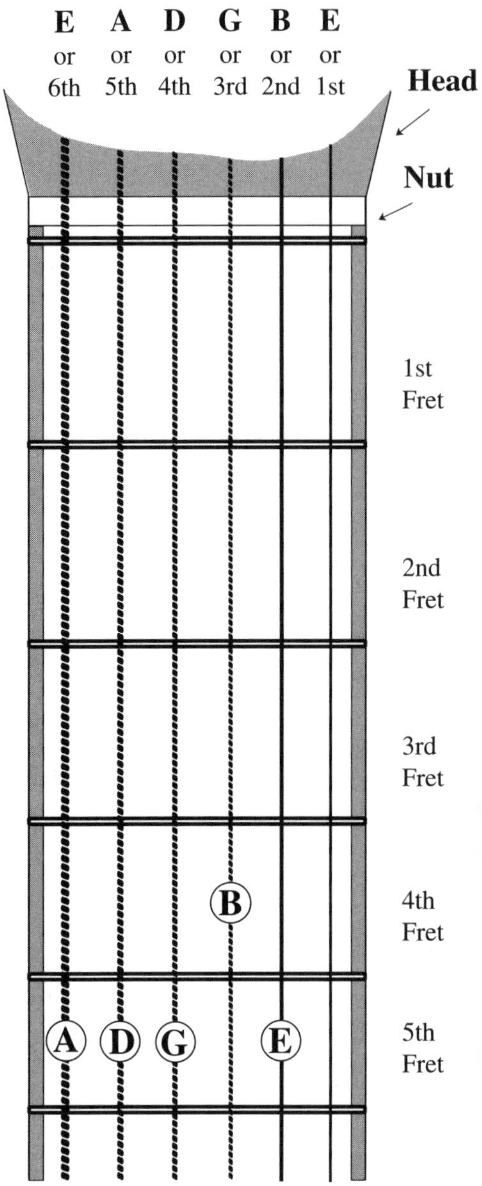

The guitar can be tuned with the aid of pitch pipes or dedicated electronic guitar tuners which are available through your local music dealer. If you do not have a tuning device, you can use relative tuning. Estimate the pitch of the 6th string as near as possible to E or at least a comfortable pitch (not too high, as you might break other strings in tuning up). Then, while checking the various positions on the diagram, place a finger from your left hand on the:

5th fret of the E or 6th string and **tune the open A** (or 5th string) to the note **(A)**

5th fret of the A or 5th string and **tune the open D** (or 4th string) to the note **(D)**

5th fret of the D or 4th string and **tune the open G** (or 3rd string) to the note **(G)**

4th fret of the G or 3rd string and **tune the open B** (or 2nd string) to the note **(B)**

5th fret of the B or 2nd string and **tune the open E** (or 1st string) to the note **(E)**

Reading Chord Boxes

Chord boxes are diagrams of the guitar neck viewed head upwards, face on as illustrated. The top horizontal line is the nut, unless a higher fret number is indicated, the others are the frets.

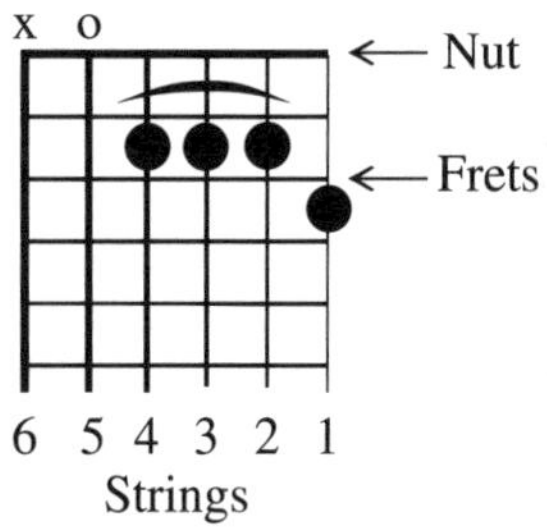

The vertical lines are the strings, starting from E (or 6th) on the left to E (or 1st) on the right.

The black dots indicate where to place your fingers.

Strings marked with an O are played open, not fretted. Strings marked with an X should not be played.

The curved bracket indicates a 'barre' – hold down the strings under the bracket with your first finger, using your other fingers to fret the remaining notes.

Loving You

Words & Music by
Jerry Leiber & Mike Stoller

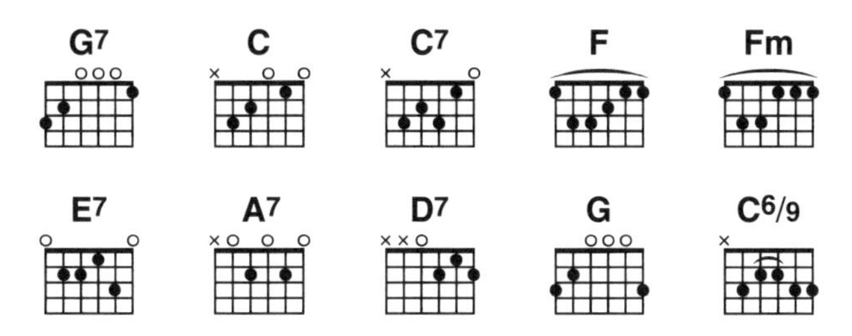

Capo first fret

Intro | G7 ||

Verse 1

```
C
I will spend my whole life through
G7
   Loving you, just loving you.

Winter, summer, spring-time, too,
C                   C7
   Loving you,   loving you.
F                              Fm                C      E7      A7
   Makes no difference   where I go or what I may  do.
D7                                          G      G7
   You know that I'll always be loving you, just you.
```

Verse 2

```
      C
And   if I'm seen with someone new,
G7
   Don't be blue, don't you be blue.

I'll be faithful, I'll be true;
C                    C7
   Always true,    true to you.
F                    Fm                C     E7      A7
   There is only one for me, and you know who.
D7                                          G   G7  C        C6/9
   You know that I'll always be lov-ing you.
```

That's All Right

Words & Music by
Arthur Crudup

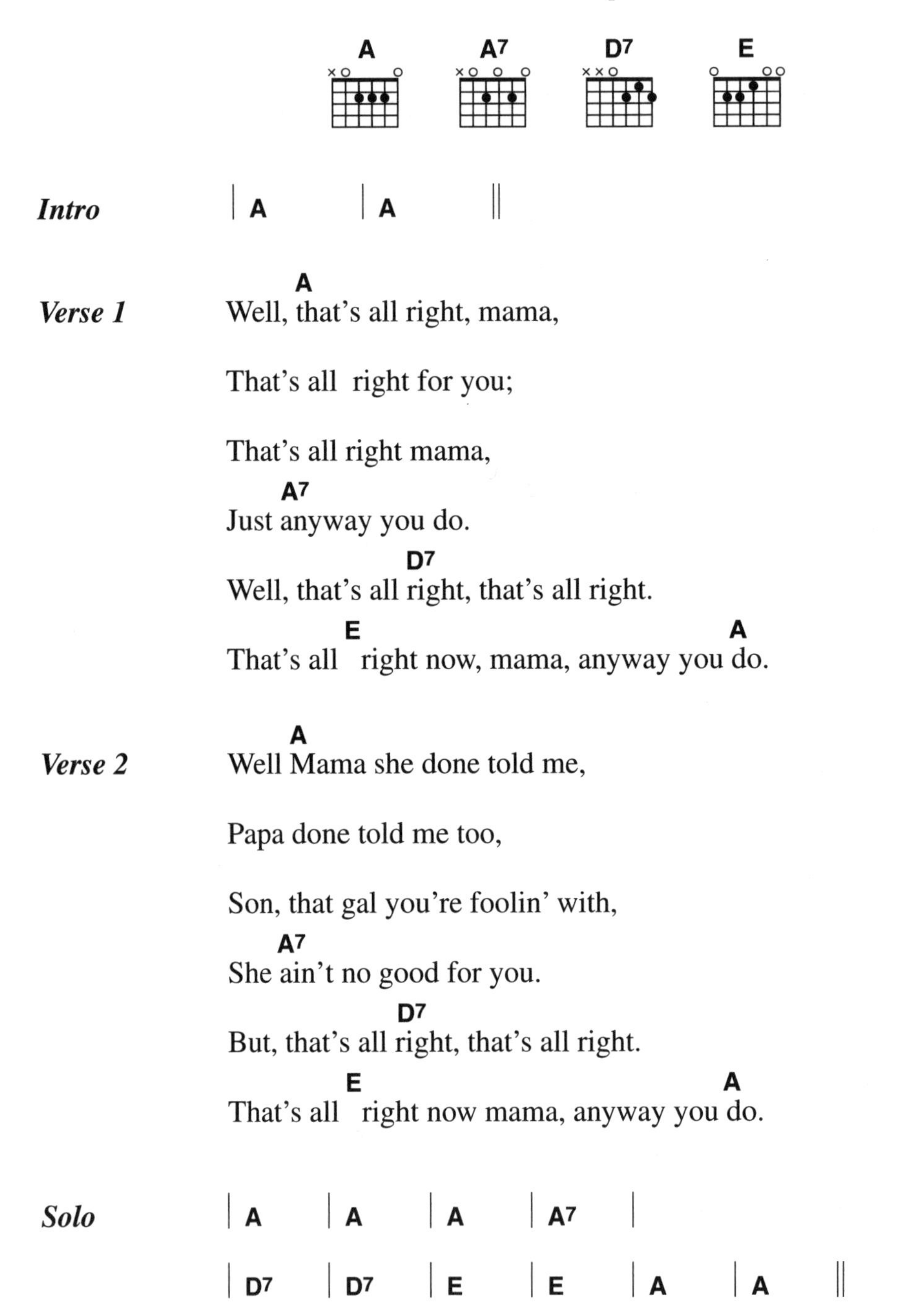

Intro | A | A ||

Verse 1

```
      A
Well, that's all right, mama,

That's all  right for you;

That's all right mama,
    A7
Just anyway you do.
                D7
Well, that's all right, that's all right.
          E                           A
That's all   right now, mama, anyway you do.
```

Verse 2

```
     A
Well Mama she done told me,

Papa done told me too,

Son, that gal you're foolin' with,
   A7
She ain't no good for you.
               D7
But, that's all right, that's all right.
          E                          A
That's all   right now mama, anyway you do.
```

Solo

| A | A | A | A7 |
| D7 | D7 | E | E | A | A ||

```
                  A
*Verse 3*   I'm leaving town, baby,

            I'm leaving town for sure.

            Well, then you won't be bothered with me
            A7
            Hanging 'round your door.
                            D7
            Well, that's all right, that's all right.
                        E                             A
            That's all  right now mama, anyway you do.


                        A
*Coda*      Ah da da dee dee dee dee, dee dee dee dee,

            Dee dee dee dee.
                           D7
            I need your loving, that's all right,
                        E                             A
            That's all  right now mama, anyway you do.

            | A       | A       ||
```

Mystery Train

Words & Music by
Sam C. Phillips & Herman Parker, Jr.

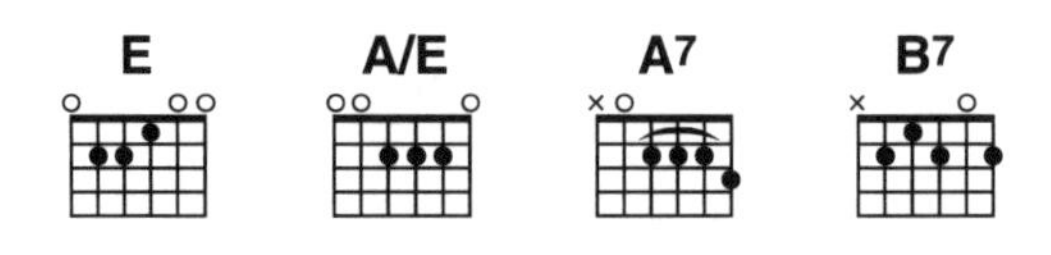

Intro | E A/E E A/E | E A/E E A/E | E A/E E A/E ||

Verse 1

```
A7                                E    A/E E A/E | E A/E E A/E |
   Train I ride, sixteen coaches long.
A7                                E    A/E E A/E | E A/E E A/E |
   Train I ride, sixteen coaches long.
          B7
Well, that long black train
A7                     E    A/E E A/E | E A/E E A/E ||
   Got my baby and gone.
```

Verse 2

```
A7
   Train train, comin' 'round,
              E     A/E E A/E | E A/E E A/E |
'Round the bend.
A7                                  E    A/E E A/E | E A/E E A/E |
   Train train, comin' 'round the bend.
         B7
Well it took my baby,
A7                      E    A/E    E  A/E | E A/E E A/E ||
   But it never will again  (no,  not a  -  gain).
```

Verse 3

```
A7                                        E    A/E E A/E | E A/E E A/E |
   Train train, comin' down, down the line.
A7                                 E    A/E E A/E | E A/E E A/E |
   Train train, comin' down the line.
          B7
Well it's bringin' my baby,
A7                                 E
   'Cause she's mine, all, all mine.
 A/E    E   A/E   E   A/E   E    A/E    E   A/E
(She's mine, _  all, all    mine. _)
```

Instrumental | A7 | A7 | E | E |

| B7 | A7 | E A/E E A/E | E A/E E A/E ||

Verse 4

A7
Train train, comin' 'round,
E A/E E A/E | E A/E E A/E |
'Round the bend.
A7 E A/E E A/E | E A/E E A/E |
Train train, comin' 'round the bend.
B7
Well it took my baby,
A7 E A/E E A/E | E A/E E A/E ||
But it never will again (never will again).

Coda | A7 | A7 | E A/E E A/E | E A/E E A/E ||

Fade out

Heartbreak Hotel

Words & Music by
Mae Boren Axton, Tommy Durden & Elvis Presley

E A B A7 B7 Fmaj7 (fr8) Emaj7 (fr7)

Verse 1

```
N.C.                              (E)
Well since my baby left me,
N.C.                                   (E)
Well I've found a new place to dwell,
N.C.
But it's down at the end of Lonely Street,

At Heartbreak Hotel, where I'll be…
```

Chorus 1

```
(A)
   I'll be so lonely, baby,

I may get so lonely,
(B)                             (E)
I may get so lonely I could die.
```

Verse 2

```
N.C.                            (E)
Although it's always crowded
N.C.                              (E)
You still can find some room
N.C.
For broken-hearted lovers

To cry there in the gloom.
```

Chorus 2

```
A7
Well they get so lonely, baby,

Well they get so lonely,
B7                                 E
They'll get so lonely they could die.
```

Verse 3

N.C. **(E)**
Now the bell-hop's tears keep flowing
N.C. **(E)**
And the desk-clerk's dressed in black,
N.C.
Well they've been so long on Lonely Street

They'll never, never look back.

Chorus 3

As Chorus 2

Verse 4

N.C. **(E)**
Well if your baby leaves you
N.C. **(E)**
And you've got a tale to tell,
N.C.
Well just take a walk down Lonely Street

To Heartbreak Hotel, where you will be…

Chorus 4

A7
Well you'll be so lonely, baby,

You'll be lonely,
B7 **E**
You'll be so lonely you could die.

Solo

| E | E | E | E |

| A7 | A7 | B7 | E ||

Verse 5

As Verse 2

Chorus 5

A7
Well they get so lonely, baby,

Well they get so lonely,
B7 **E** **Fmaj7** **Emaj7**
Where they'll be so lonely they could die.

Blue Suede Shoes

Words & Music by
Carl Lee Perkins

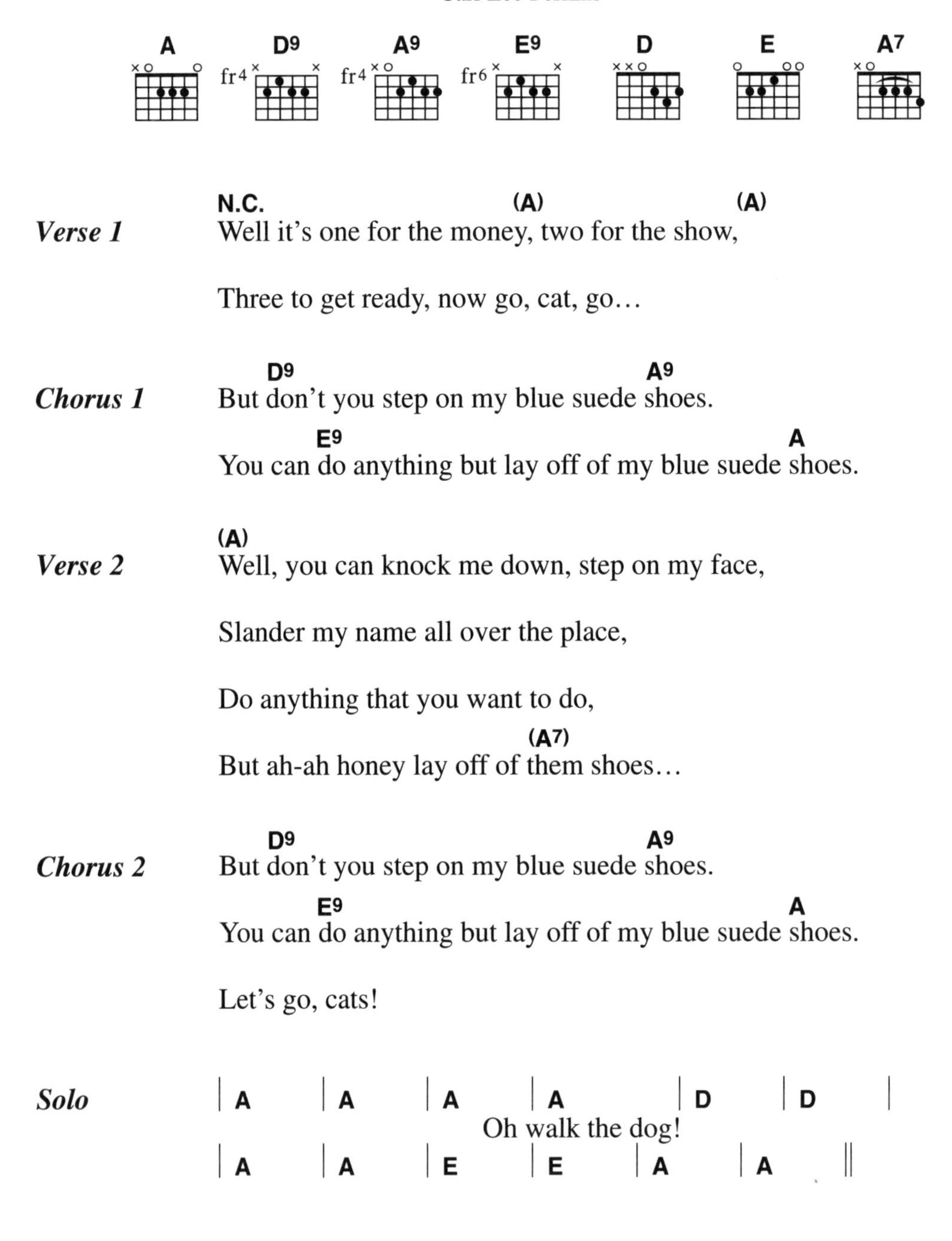

Verse 1

N.C. (A) (A)
Well it's one for the money, two for the show,

Three to get ready, now go, cat, go…

Chorus 1

D9 A9
But don't you step on my blue suede shoes.
E9 A
You can do anything but lay off of my blue suede shoes.

Verse 2

(A)
Well, you can knock me down, step on my face,

Slander my name all over the place,

Do anything that you want to do,
(A7)
But ah-ah honey lay off of them shoes…

Chorus 2

D9 A9
But don't you step on my blue suede shoes.
E9 A
You can do anything but lay off of my blue suede shoes.

Let's go, cats!

Solo

| A | A | A | A | D | D |
Oh walk the dog!
| A | A | E | E | A | A ||

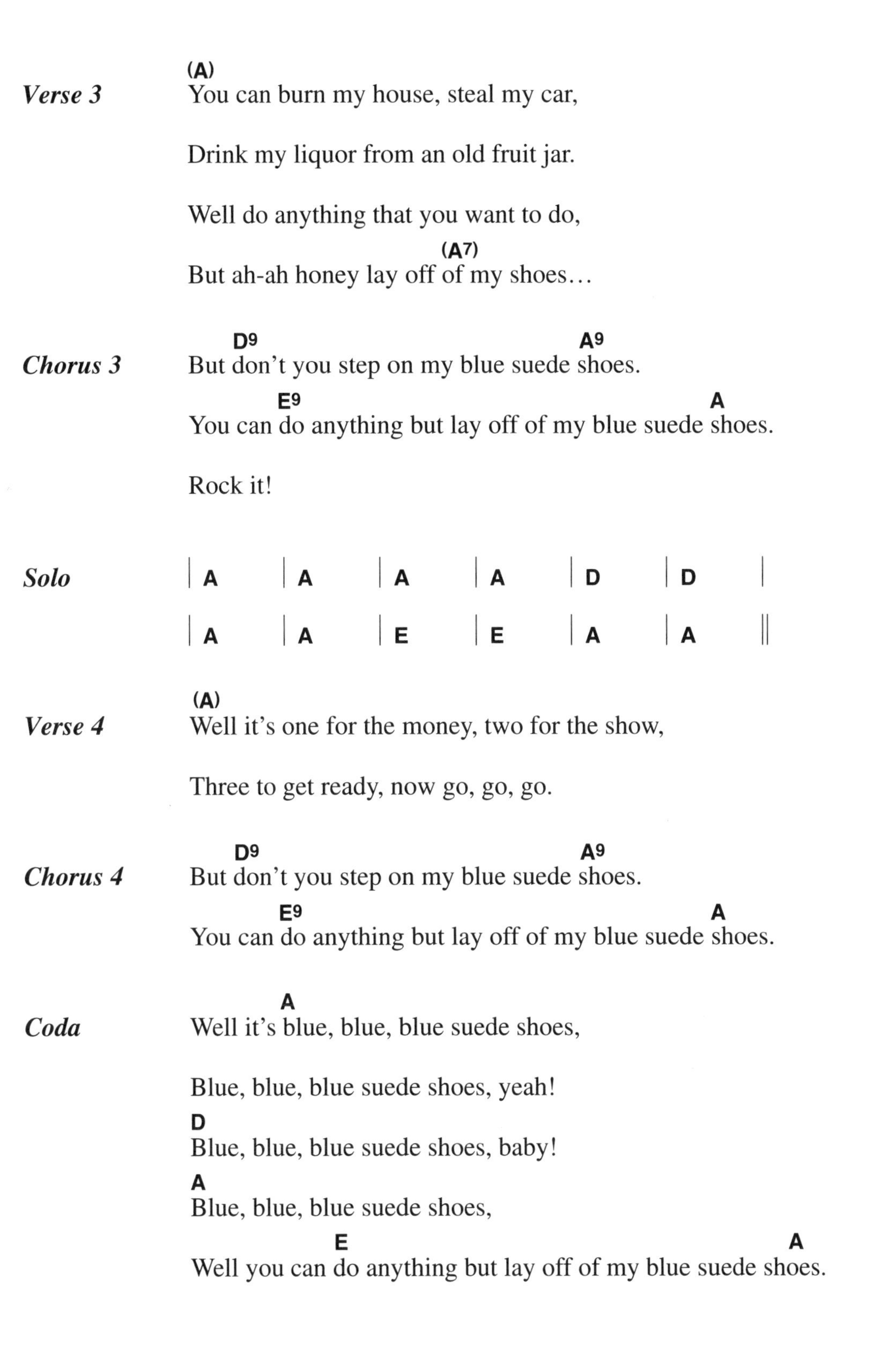

Verse 3

(A)
You can burn my house, steal my car,

Drink my liquor from an old fruit jar.

Well do anything that you want to do,

(A7)
But ah-ah honey lay off of my shoes…

Chorus 3

D9 A9
But don't you step on my blue suede shoes.

E9 A
You can do anything but lay off of my blue suede shoes.

Rock it!

Solo

A	A	A	A	D	D
A	A	E	E	A	A

Verse 4

(A)
Well it's one for the money, two for the show,

Three to get ready, now go, go, go.

Chorus 4

D9 A9
But don't you step on my blue suede shoes.

E9 A
You can do anything but lay off of my blue suede shoes.

Coda

A
Well it's blue, blue, blue suede shoes,

Blue, blue, blue suede shoes, yeah!

D
Blue, blue, blue suede shoes, baby!

A
Blue, blue, blue suede shoes,

E A
Well you can do anything but lay off of my blue suede shoes.

Lawdy, Miss Clawdy

Words & Music by
Lloyd Price

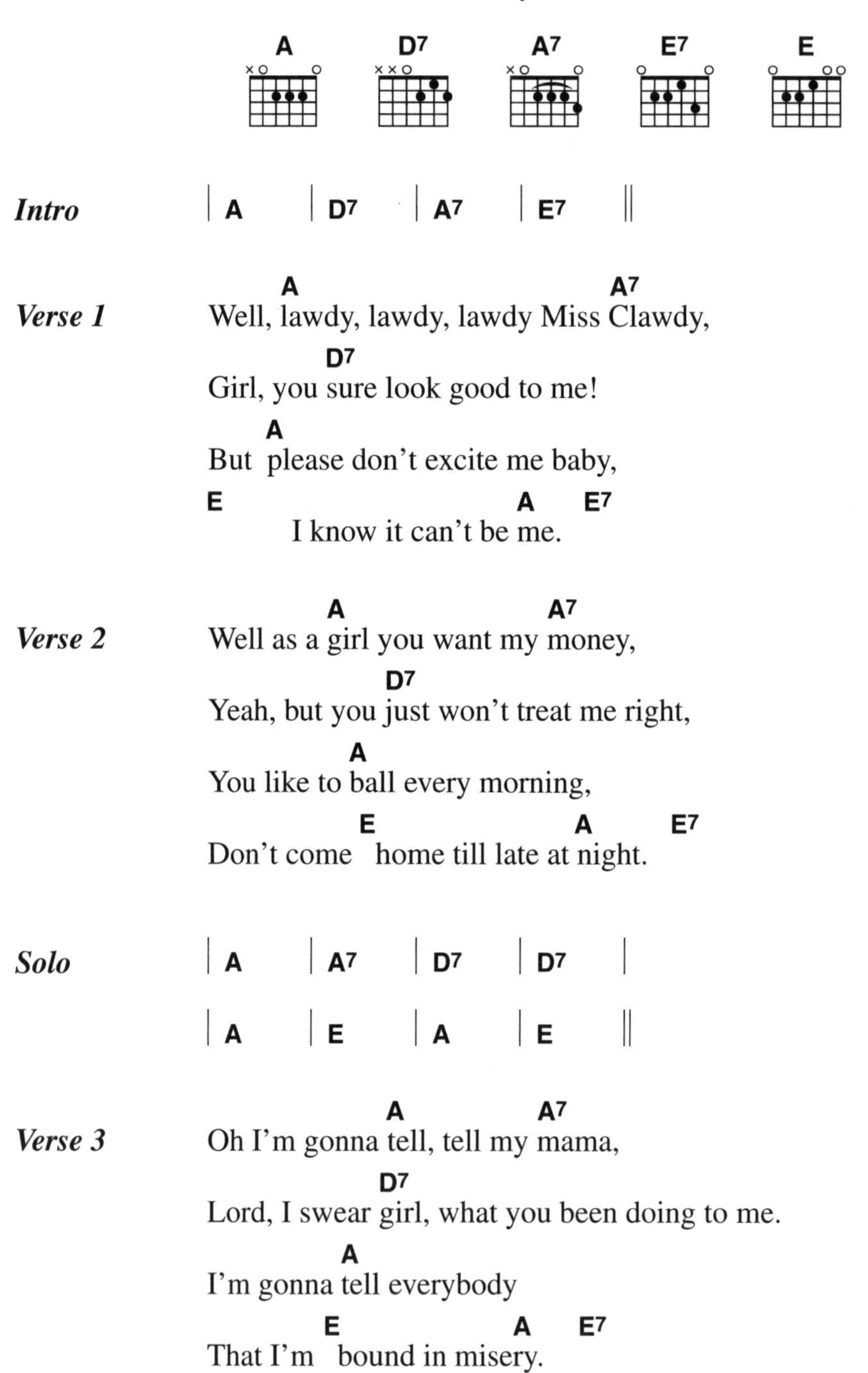

Intro | A | D7 | A7 | E7 ||

Verse 1

A A7
Well, lawdy, lawdy, lawdy Miss Clawdy,
D7
Girl, you sure look good to me!
A
But please don't excite me baby,
E A E7
I know it can't be me.

Verse 2

A A7
Well as a girl you want my money,
D7
Yeah, but you just won't treat me right,
A
You like to ball every morning,
E A E7
Don't come home till late at night.

Solo | A | A7 | D7 | D7 |

| A | E | A | E ||

Verse 3

A A7
Oh I'm gonna tell, tell my mama,
D7
Lord, I swear girl, what you been doing to me.
A
I'm gonna tell everybody
E A E7
That I'm bound in misery.

Verse 4

A A7
So bye, bye, bye, baby,
D7
Girl, I won't be comin' no more.
A
Goodbye little darlin',
E A E7
Down the road I'll go.

Piano link | A | D7 | A7 | E7 ||

Verse 5

A A7
So bye, bye, bye, baby,
D7
Girl, I won't be comin' no more.
A
Goodbye little darlin',
E A E7 A D7 A
Down the road I'll go.

Hound Dog

Words & Music by
Jerry Leiber & Mike Stoller

C | F7 | G (fr3) | F | D♭ (fr9) | C* (fr8)

Chorus 1

```
N.C.                          C
You ain't nothing but a hound dog, crying all the time.
                              F7                     C
You ain't nothing but a hound dog, crying all the time.
             G
Well, you ain't never caught a rabbit
            F              C
And you ain't no friend of mine.
```

Verse 1

```
N.C.                          C
Well they said you was high class, well that was just a lie,
                              F7                         C
Yeah they said you was high class, well that was just a lie.
             G
Yeah, you ain't never caught a rabbit
            F              C
And you ain't no friend of mine.
```

Chorus 2

As Chorus 1

Solo

```
| C  | C  | C  | C  | F7 | F7 |
| C  | C  | G  | F  | C  | C  ||
```

Verse 2

```
                              C
Well they said you was high class, well that was just a lie,
                              F7                         C
Yeah they said you was high class, well that was just a lie.
             G
Yeah, you ain't never caught a rabbit
            F              C
And you ain't no friend of mine.
```

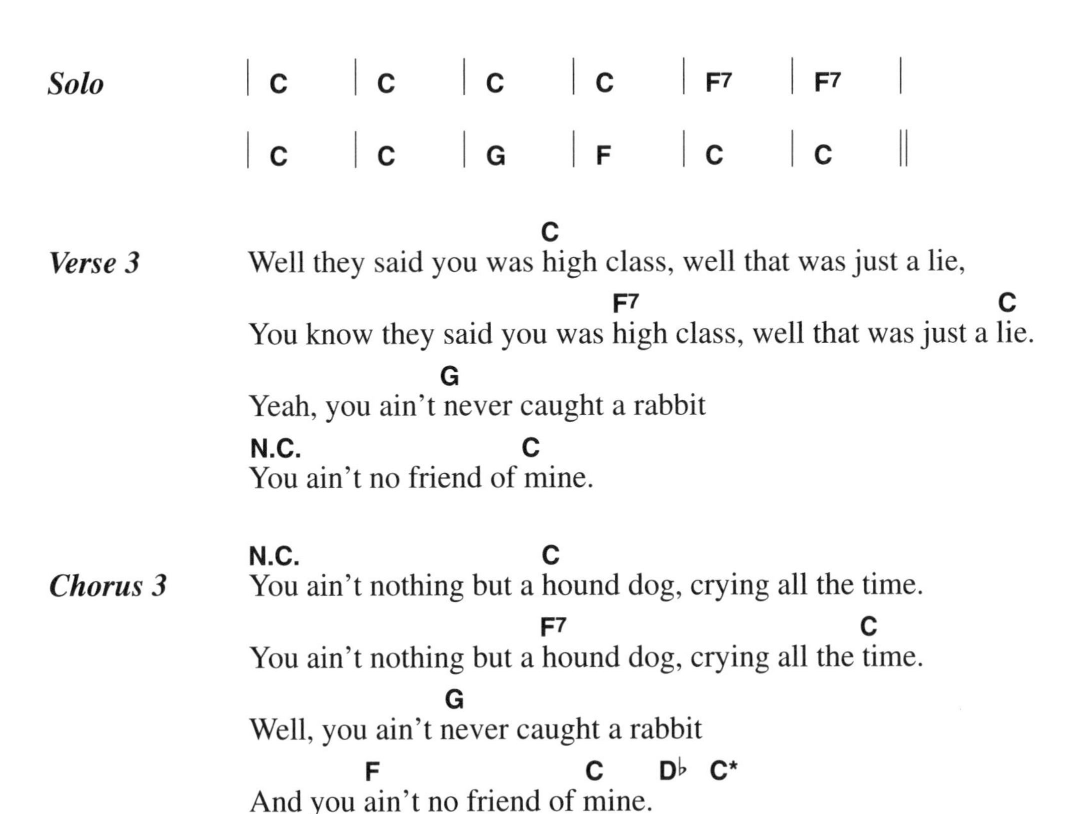

Solo | C | C | C | C | F7 | F7 |

| C | C | G | F | C | C ||

Verse 3

C
Well they said you was high class, well that was just a lie,

F7 C
You know they said you was high class, well that was just a lie.

G
Yeah, you ain't never caught a rabbit

N.C. C
You ain't no friend of mine.

Chorus 3

N.C. C
You ain't nothing but a hound dog, crying all the time.

F7 C
You ain't nothing but a hound dog, crying all the time.

G
Well, you ain't never caught a rabbit

F C D♭ C*
And you ain't no friend of mine.

Don't Be Cruel

Words & Music by
Otis Blackwell & Elvis Presley

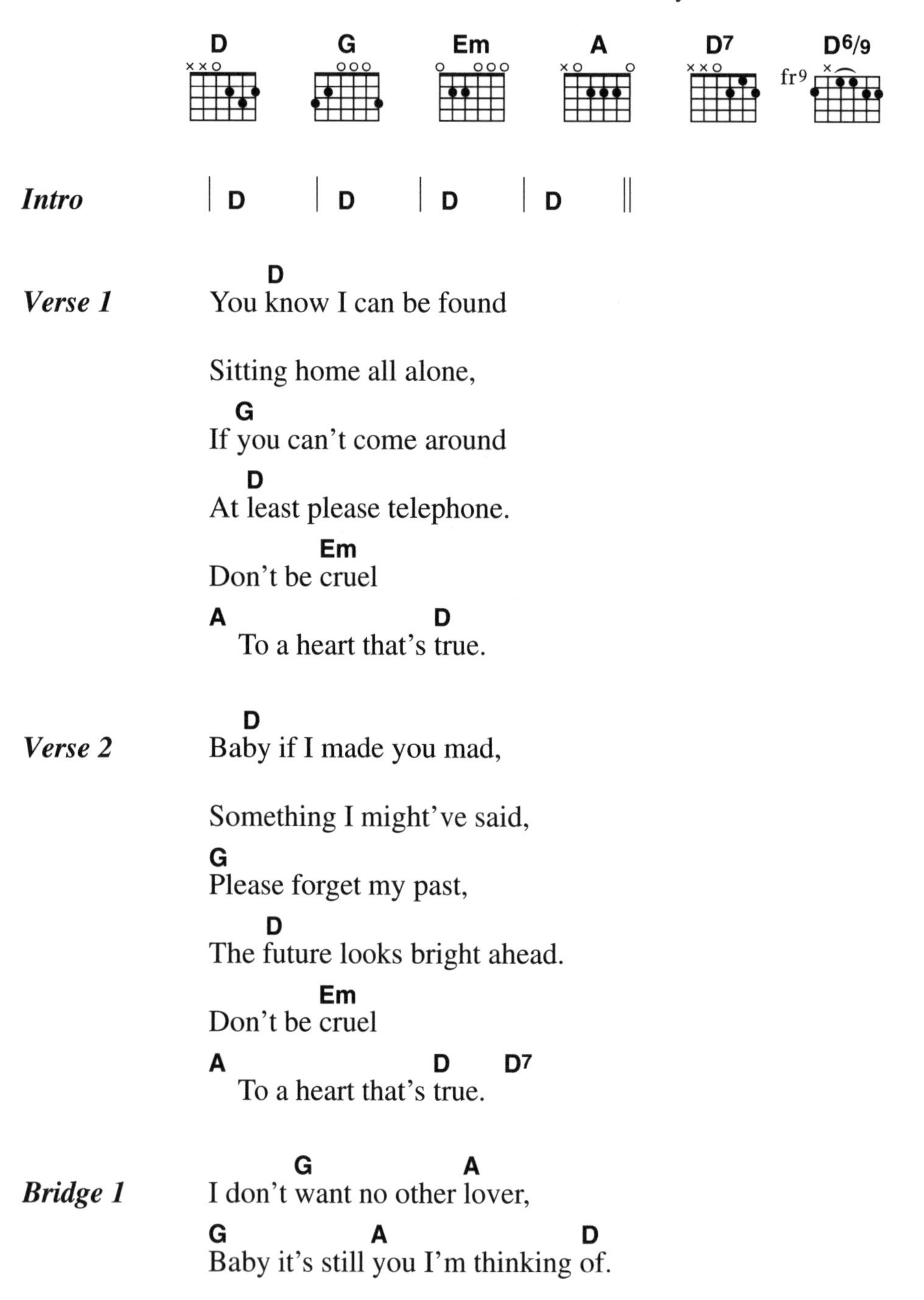

Intro | D | D | D | D ||

Verse 1

```
        D
You know I can be found
Sitting home all alone,
  G
If you can't come around
 D
At least please telephone.
           Em
Don't be cruel
A                D
  To a heart that's true.
```

Verse 2

```
  D
Baby if I made you mad,
Something I might've said,
G
Please forget my past,
    D
The future looks bright ahead.
           Em
Don't be cruel
A                D     D7
  To a heart that's true.
```

Bridge 1

```
         G            A
I don't want no other lover,
G          A            D
Baby it's still you I'm thinking of.
```

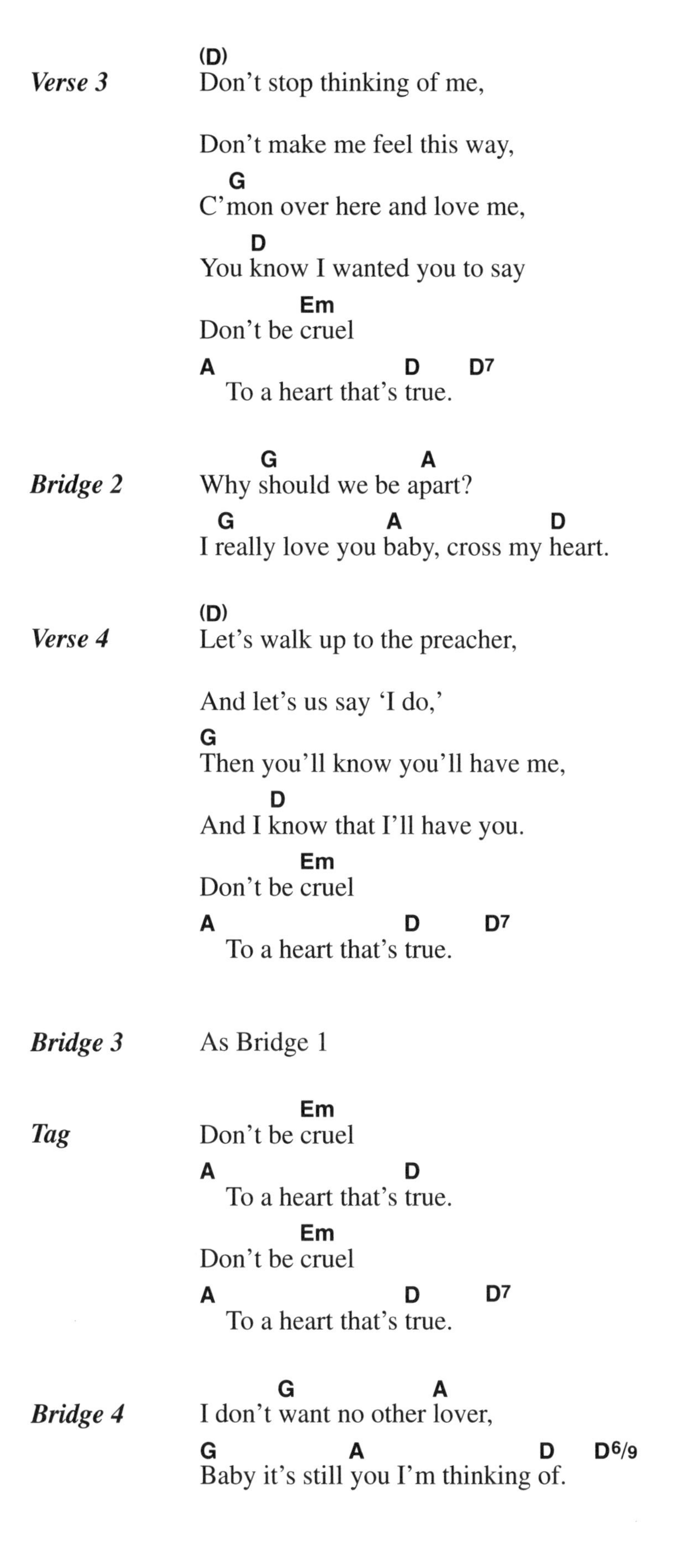

Verse 3

(D)
Don't stop thinking of me,

Don't make me feel this way,

G
C'mon over here and love me,

D
You know I wanted you to say

Em
Don't be cruel

A D D7
To a heart that's true.

Bridge 2

G A
Why should we be apart?

G A D
I really love you baby, cross my heart.

Verse 4

(D)
Let's walk up to the preacher,

And let's us say 'I do,'

G
Then you'll know you'll have me,

D
And I know that I'll have you.

Em
Don't be cruel

A D D7
To a heart that's true.

Bridge 3

As Bridge 1

Tag

Em
Don't be cruel

A D
To a heart that's true.

Em
Don't be cruel

A D D7
To a heart that's true.

Bridge 4

G A
I don't want no other lover,

G A D D6/9
Baby it's still you I'm thinking of.

Love Me Tender

Words & Music by
Elvis Presley & Vera Matson

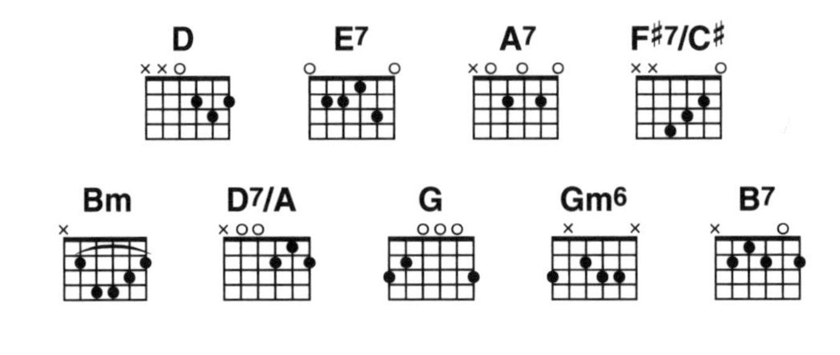

Intro | D ||

Verse 1

D E7
Love me tender, love me sweet,
A7 D
Never let me go.
E7
You have made my life complete
A7 D
And I love you so.

Chorus 1

F♯7/C♯ Bm D7/A
Love me tender, love me true,
G Gm6 D
All my dreams fulfilled.
B7 E7
For my darling I love you
A7 D
And I always will.

Verse 2

D E7
Love me tender, love me long,
A7 D
Take me to your heart.
E7
For it's there that I belong
A7 D
And will never part.

Chorus 2

```
         F♯7/C♯  Bm      D7/A
Love me tender, love me true,

G       Gm6       D
All my dreams fulfilled.

        B7     E7
For my darling I love you

A7            D
And I always will.
```

Verse 3

```
D               E7
Love me tender, love me dear,

A7              D
Tell me you are mine.

                    E7
I'll be yours through all the years

A7             D
Till the end of time.
```

Chorus 3

```
         F♯7/C♯  Bm      D7/A
Love me tender, love me true,

G       Gm6       D
All my dreams fulfilled.

        B7     E7
For my darling I love you

A7            D
And I always will.
```

Too Much

Words & Music by
Lee Rosenberg & Bernard Weinman

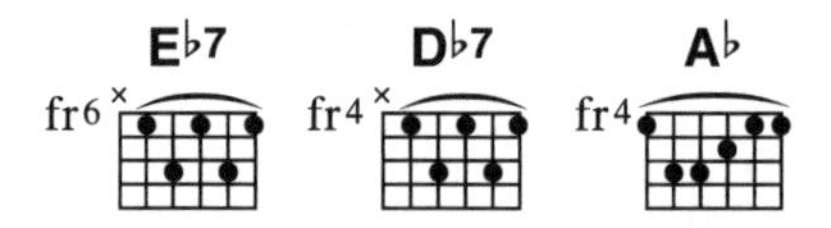

Tune guitar slightly sharp

Intro | E♭7 | D♭7 | A♭ | A♭ ||

Verse 1
A♭
Well Honey, I love you too much,

I need your lovin' too much;
D♭7
Want the thrill of your touch,
A♭
Gee, I can't love you too much.
E♭7
You do all the livin'
D♭7
While I do all the givin'
A♭ E♭7
'Cause I love you too much.

Verse 2
A♭
Well you spend all my money too much,

I have to share you honey, too much.
D♭7
When I want some lovin', you're gone.
A♭
Don't you know you're treatin' your Daddy wrong.
E♭7
Now you got me started
D♭7
Don't you leave me broken hearted
A♭ E♭7
'Cause I love you too much.

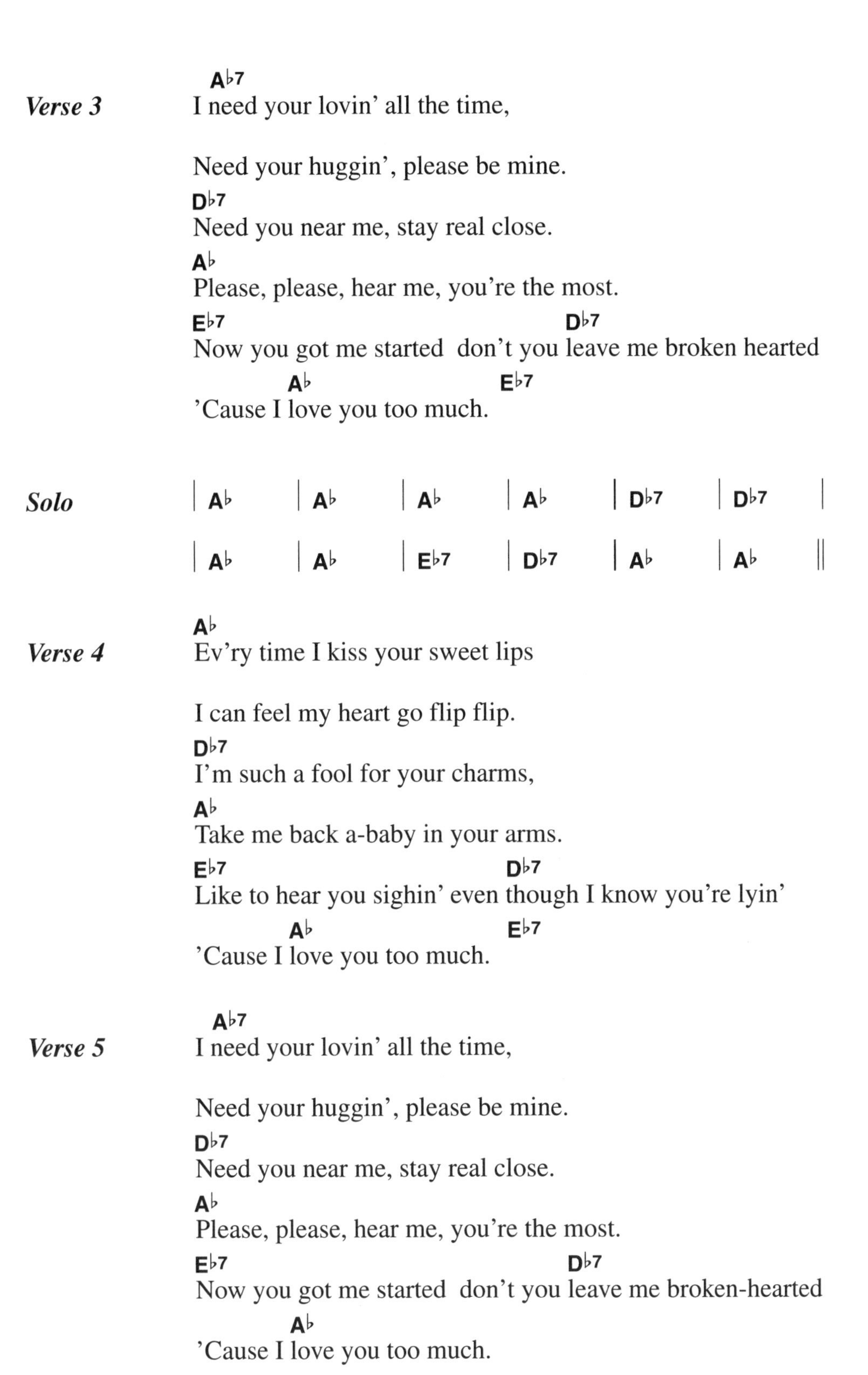

Verse 3

A♭7
I need your lovin' all the time,

Need your huggin', please be mine.
D♭7
Need you near me, stay real close.
A♭
Please, please, hear me, you're the most.
E♭7 D♭7
Now you got me started don't you leave me broken hearted
A♭ E♭7
'Cause I love you too much.

Solo

| A♭ | A♭ | A♭ | A♭ | D♭7 | D♭7 |
| A♭ | A♭ | E♭7 | D♭7 | A♭ | A♭ ||

Verse 4

A♭
Ev'ry time I kiss your sweet lips

I can feel my heart go flip flip.
D♭7
I'm such a fool for your charms,
A♭
Take me back a-baby in your arms.
E♭7 D♭7
Like to hear you sighin' even though I know you're lyin'
A♭ E♭7
'Cause I love you too much.

Verse 5

A♭7
I need your lovin' all the time,

Need your huggin', please be mine.
D♭7
Need you near me, stay real close.
A♭
Please, please, hear me, you're the most.
E♭7 D♭7
Now you got me started don't you leave me broken-hearted
A♭
'Cause I love you too much.

All Shook Up

Words & Music by
Otis Blackwell & Elvis Presley

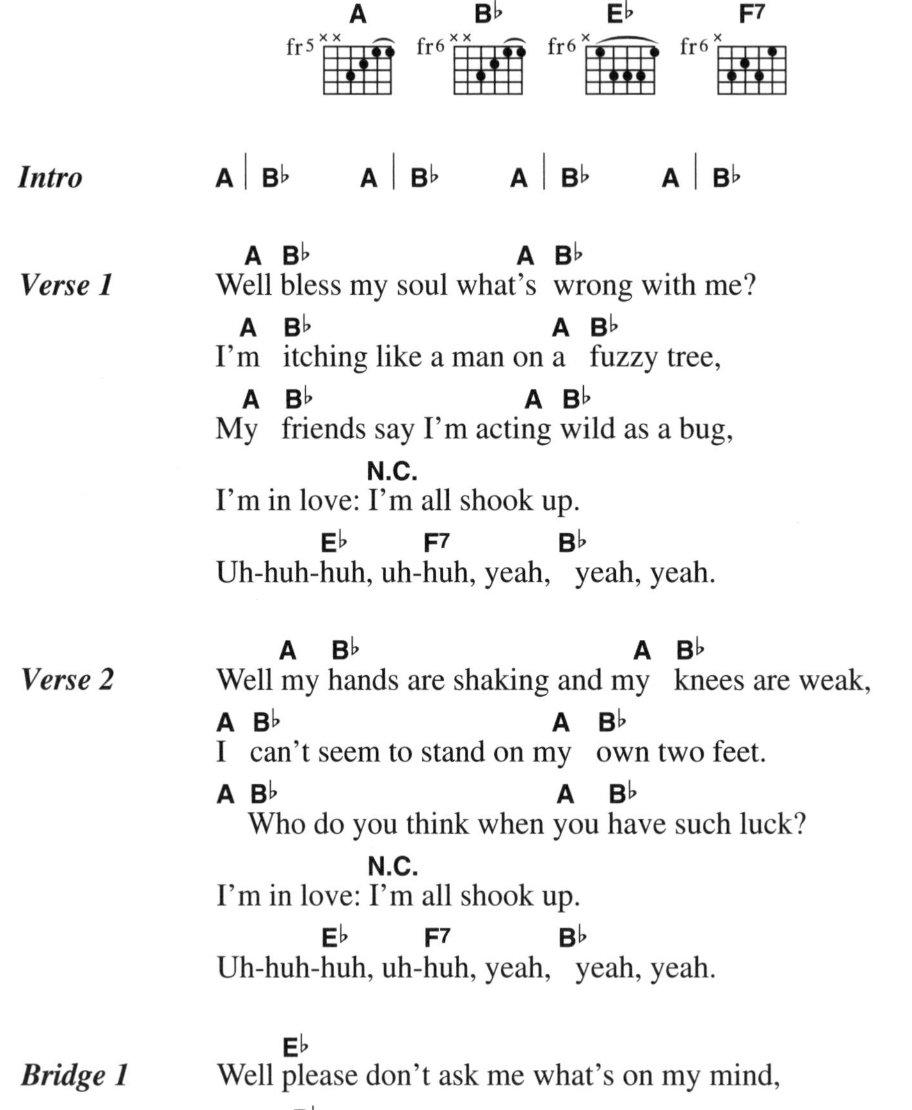

Intro A | B♭ A | B♭ A | B♭ A | B♭

Verse 1

A B♭ A B♭
Well bless my soul what's wrong with me?
A B♭ A B♭
I'm itching like a man on a fuzzy tree,
A B♭ A B♭
My friends say I'm acting wild as a bug,
N.C.
I'm in love: I'm all shook up.
E♭ F7 B♭
Uh-huh-huh, uh-huh, yeah, yeah, yeah.

Verse 2

A B♭ A B♭
Well my hands are shaking and my knees are weak,
A B♭ A B♭
I can't seem to stand on my own two feet.
A B♭ A B♭
Who do you think when you have such luck?
N.C.
I'm in love: I'm all shook up.
E♭ F7 B♭
Uh-huh-huh, uh-huh, yeah, yeah, yeah.

Bridge 1

E♭
Well please don't ask me what's on my mind,
B♭
I'm a little mixed up but I feel fine.
E♭
Well I met a girl that I love best,
F7 N.C.
My heart beats so that it scares me to death.

```
             A    B♭                          A    B♭
*Verse 3*    When she   touch my hand, what a    chill I got,

              A    B♭                    A   B♭
             Her   lips are like a vol - cano that's hot,

             A    B♭                      A   B♭
                I'm proud to say she's my    buttercup.

                         N.C.
             I'm in love: I'm all shook up.

                       E♭       F7            B♭
             Uh-huh-huh, uh-huh, yeah,    yeah, yeah.
```

```
                 E♭
*Bridge 2*   My tongue gets tired when I try to speak,

                 B♭
             My insides shake like a leaf on a tree,

                     E♭
             There's only one cure for this body of mine,

                       F7   N.C.
             That's to have that girl and a love so fine.
```

Verse 4   As Verse 3

```
                      E♭       F          B♭
             Uh-huh-huh, uh-huh, yeah, yeah, yeah.
                      E♭       F          B♭
             Uh-huh-huh, uh-huh, yeah, yeah,

             I'm all shook up.
```

Teddy Bear

Words & Music by
Kal Mann & Bernie Lowe

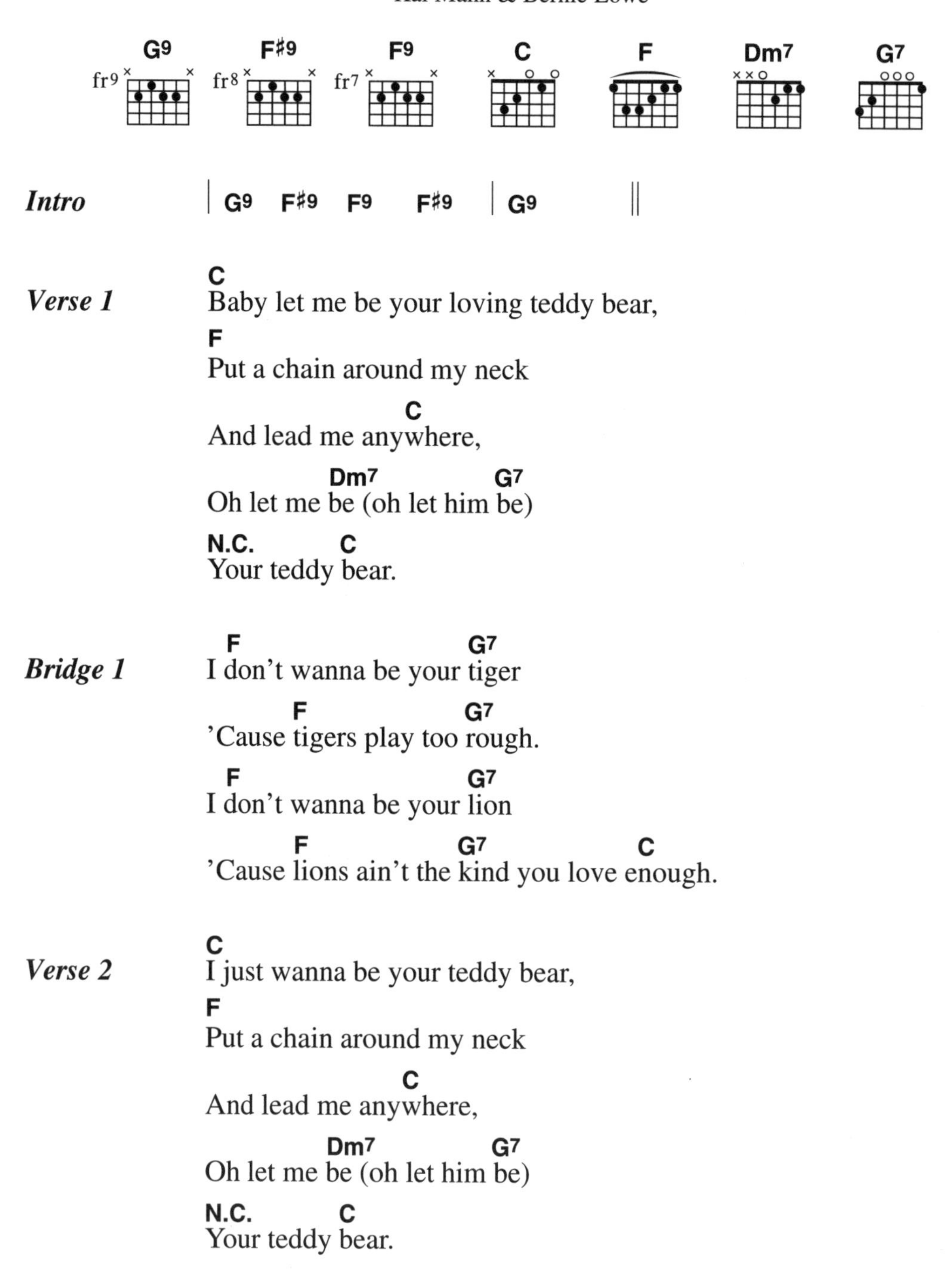

Intro | G9 F♯9 F9 F♯9 | G9 ||

Verse 1

C
Baby let me be your loving teddy bear,
F
Put a chain around my neck
                C
And lead me anywhere,
             Dm7   G7
Oh let me be (oh let him be)
N.C.   C
Your teddy bear.

Bridge 1

 F   G7
I don't wanna be your tiger
        F   G7
'Cause tigers play too rough.
 F   G7
I don't wanna be your lion
        F   G7   C
'Cause lions ain't the kind you love enough.

Verse 2

C
I just wanna be your teddy bear,
F
Put a chain around my neck
                C
And lead me anywhere,
             Dm7   G7
Oh let me be (oh let him be)
N.C.   C
Your teddy bear.

Verse 3

```
C
Baby let me be around you every night,
F
Run your fingers through my hair
                        C
And cuddle me real tight.
          Dm7           G7
Oh let me be (oh let him be)
N.C.      C
Your teddy bear.
```

Bridge 2

As Bridge 1

Verse 4

```
          C
Just wanna be your teddy bear,
F
Put a chain around my neck
                   C
And lead me anywhere.
          Dm7           G7
Oh let me be (oh let him be)
N.C.      C
Your teddy bear
          G7
Oh let me be (oh let him be)
          C
Your teddy bear. __
(C)
I just wanna be your teddy bear.
```

Party

Words & Music by
Jessie Mae Robinson

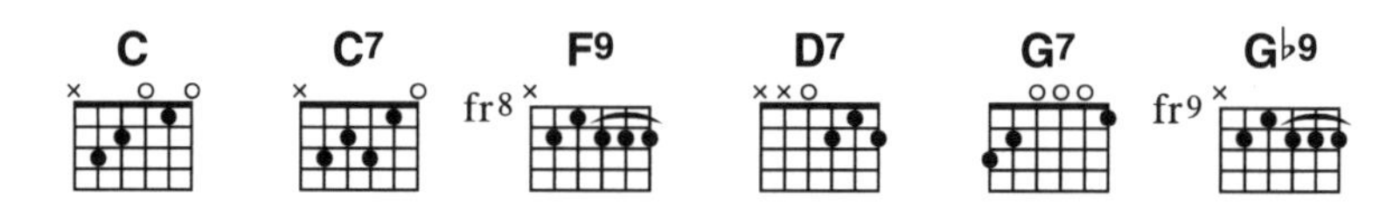


```
            N.C.                 C
Verse 1     Some people like to rock,
            N.C.                C
            Some people like to roll

             But movin' and a-groovin'
                C7
            Gonna satisfy my soul.

                          F9
Chorus 1    Let's have a party, whooo!
                           C
            Let's have a party.
            D7         G7       C
            Send to the store, let's   buy some more,
                D7          G7      C
            Let's   have a party tonight.

             C   N.C.              G♭9
Verse 2     I never kissed a bear,
             F9     N.C.              F9
            I never kissed a goon,
                C
            But I can shake a chicken
                     C7
            In the middle of the room.


Chorus 2    As Chorus 1
```

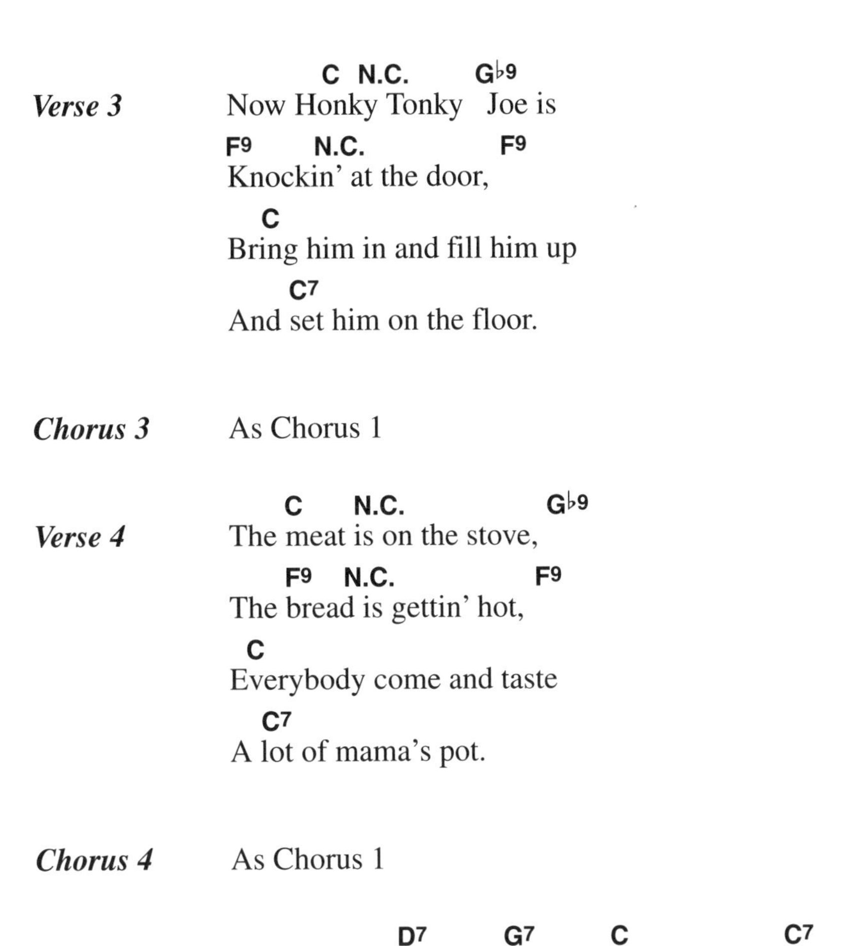

Verse 3

C N.C. G♭9
Now Honky Tonky Joe is
F9 N.C. F9
Knockin' at the door,
C
Bring him in and fill him up
C7
And set him on the floor.

Chorus 3 As Chorus 1

Verse 4

C N.C. G♭9
The meat is on the stove,
F9 N.C. F9
The bread is gettin' hot,
C
Everybody come and taste
C7
A lot of mama's pot.

Chorus 4 As Chorus 1

Coda

D7 G7 C C7
We're gonna have a party tonight. ________

Jailhouse Rock

Words & Music by
Jerry Leiber & Mike Stoller

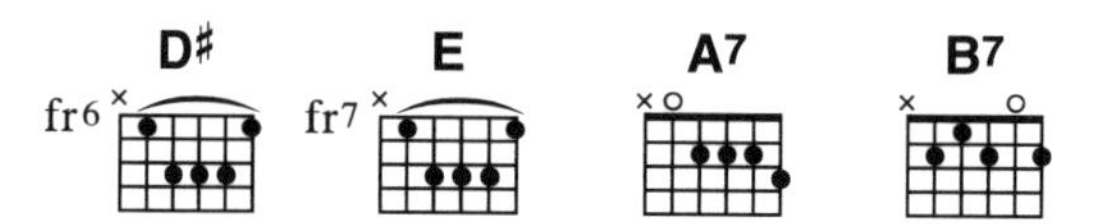

Tune guitar down one semitone

Intro | D♯ | E D♯ | E D♯ ||

Verse 1

```
     E
     Warden threw a party in the County jail:
D♯       E
     The prison band was there, they began to wail;
D♯       E
     The band was jumpin' and the drummer began to swing,
D♯       E         N.C.
     You should've heard those knocked-out jail-birds sing.
```

Chorus 1

```
    A7                       E
Let's rock, everybody let's rock.
     B7                       A7
Everybody in the whole cell block
    E
Was dancing to the jailhouse rock.
```

Verse 2

```
D♯  E
     Spider Murphy played his tenor saxophone,
D♯  E
     Little Joe was blowin' on the slide trombone.
D♯       E
     The drummer brought from Illinois went crash boom bang,
D♯       E       N.C.
     The whole rhythm section was a purple gang.
```

Chorus 2 As Chorus 1

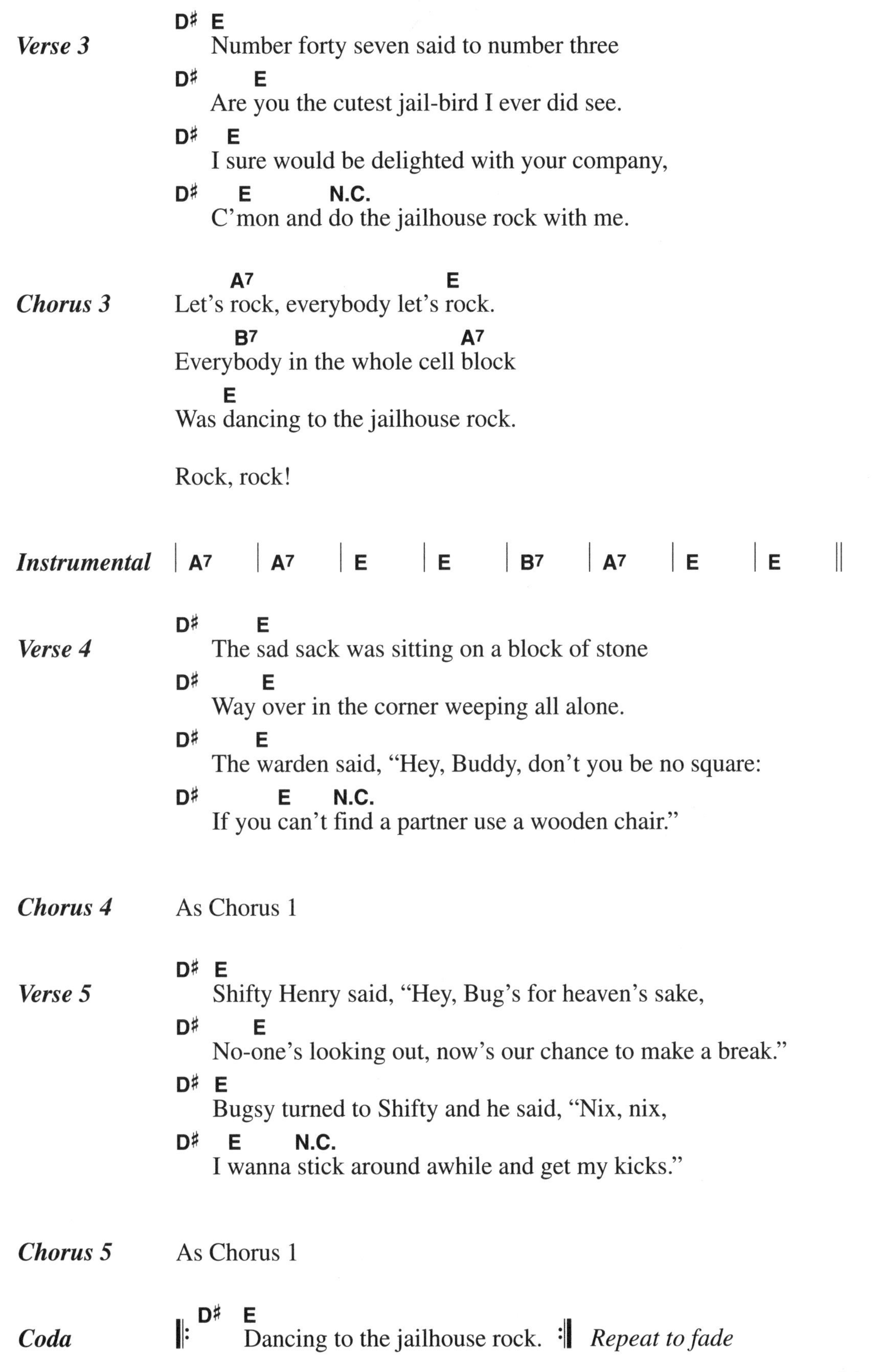

Verse 3

D♯ E
Number forty seven said to number three
D♯ E
Are you the cutest jail-bird I ever did see.
D♯ E
I sure would be delighted with your company,
D♯ E N.C.
C'mon and do the jailhouse rock with me.

Chorus 3

A7 E
Let's rock, everybody let's rock.
B7 A7
Everybody in the whole cell block
E
Was dancing to the jailhouse rock.

Rock, rock!

Instrumental | A7 | A7 | E | E | B7 | A7 | E | E ||

Verse 4

D♯ E
The sad sack was sitting on a block of stone
D♯ E
Way over in the corner weeping all alone.
D♯ E
The warden said, "Hey, Buddy, don't you be no square:
D♯ E N.C.
If you can't find a partner use a wooden chair."

Chorus 4 As Chorus 1

Verse 5

D♯ E
Shifty Henry said, "Hey, Bug's for heaven's sake,
D♯ E
No-one's looking out, now's our chance to make a break."
D♯ E
Bugsy turned to Shifty and he said, "Nix, nix,
D♯ E N.C.
I wanna stick around awhile and get my kicks."

Chorus 5 As Chorus 1

Coda

D♯ E
𝄆 Dancing to the jailhouse rock. 𝄇 *Repeat to fade*

Don’t

Words & Music by
Jerry Leiber & Mike Stoller

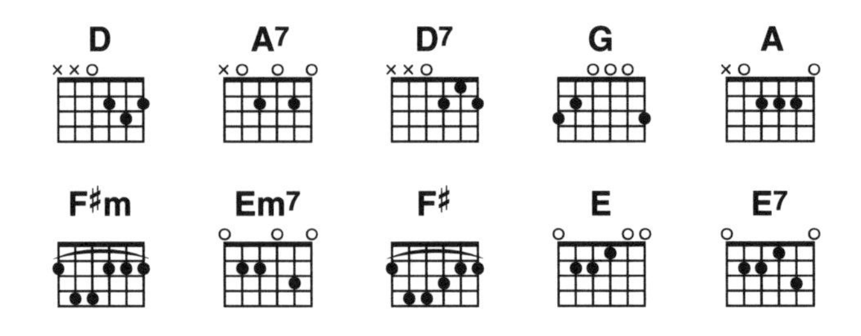

Verse 1

D A7
Don’t (don't), don’t (don't),
D7 G
That’s what you say
A D F♯m Em7 A7
Each time that I hold you this way.
D
When I feel like this
D7 G Em7
And I want to kiss you, baby,
A D
Don’t say don’t.
Em7 A7
(Don’t, don’t.)

Verse 2

D A7
Don’t (don't), don’t (don't),
D7 G
Leave my embrace
A D F♯m Em7 A7
For here in my arms is your place.
D
When the night grows cold
D7 G Em7
And I want to hold you baby
A D
Don’t say don’t.
D7
(Don’t, don’t, don’t, don’t.) ___

```
        G                 F#
Bridge  If you think that this
           G    A    D          D7
        Is just   a    game I'm playing,
        E
        If you think that
                        A      E7        A7
        I don't mean every word I'm saying.

        D                A7
Verse 3 Don't (don't), don't (don't)
        D7                 G
        Don't feel that way.
        A   D               F#m       Em7    A7
        I'm your love and yours I will stay
                          D
        This you can believe:
               D7    G
        I will never leave you,
        Em7      A        D       Em7
        Heaven knows I won't,
        A7                D
        Baby, don't say don't.
         G               D
        (Don't, please don't.)
```

Trouble

Words & Music by
Jerry Leiber & Mike Stoller

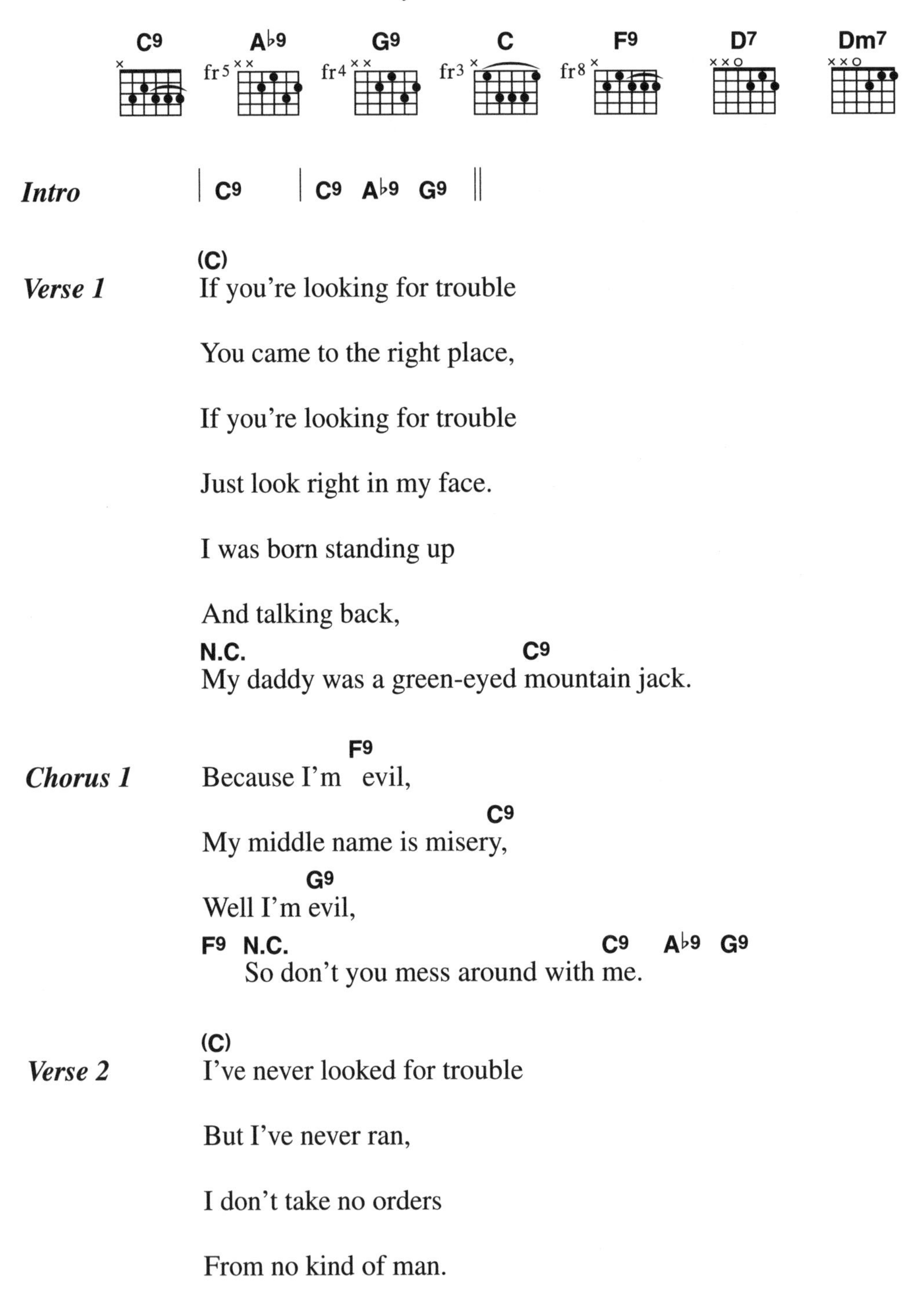

Intro | C9 | C9 A♭9 G9 ||

Verse 1

(C)
If you're looking for trouble

You came to the right place,

If you're looking for trouble

Just look right in my face.

I was born standing up

And talking back,

N.C. C9
My daddy was a green-eyed mountain jack.

Chorus 1

F9
Because I'm evil,

C9
My middle name is misery,

G9
Well I'm evil,

F9 N.C. C9 A♭9 G9
So don't you mess around with me.

Verse 2

(C)
I've never looked for trouble

But I've never ran,

I don't take no orders

From no kind of man.

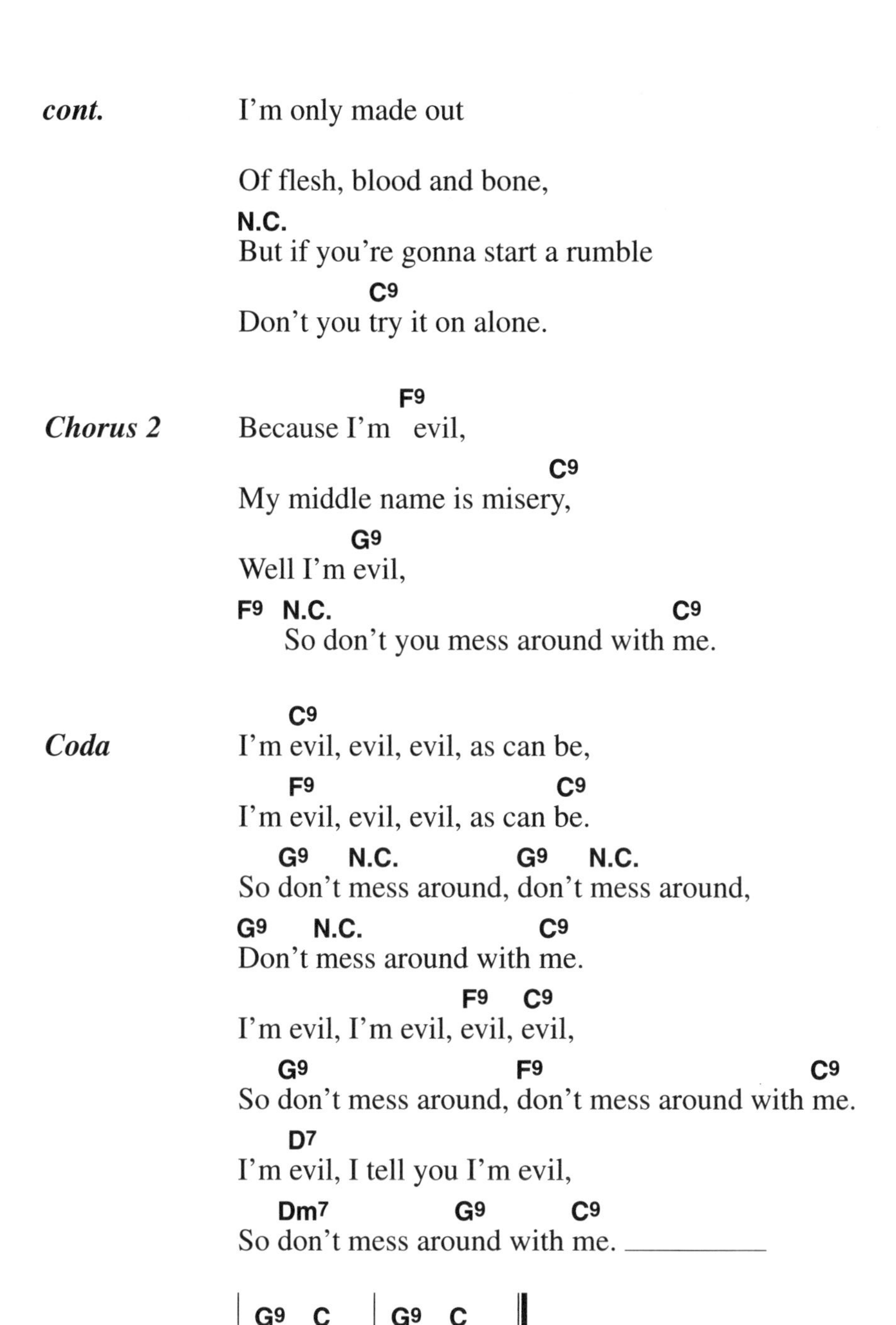

cont.

I'm only made out

Of flesh, blood and bone,

N.C.
But if you're gonna start a rumble

C9
Don't you try it on alone.

Chorus 2

F9
Because I'm evil,

C9
My middle name is misery,

G9
Well I'm evil,

F9 N.C. C9
So don't you mess around with me.

Coda

C9
I'm evil, evil, evil, as can be,

F9 C9
I'm evil, evil, evil, as can be.

G9 N.C. G9 N.C.
So don't mess around, don't mess around,

G9 N.C. C9
Don't mess around with me.

F9 C9
I'm evil, I'm evil, evil, evil,

G9 F9 C9
So don't mess around, don't mess around with me.

D7
I'm evil, I tell you I'm evil,

Dm7 G9 C9
So don't mess around with me. _________

| G9 C | G9 C ||
Yeah!

Wear My Ring Around Your Neck

Words & Music by
Bert Carroll & Russell Moody

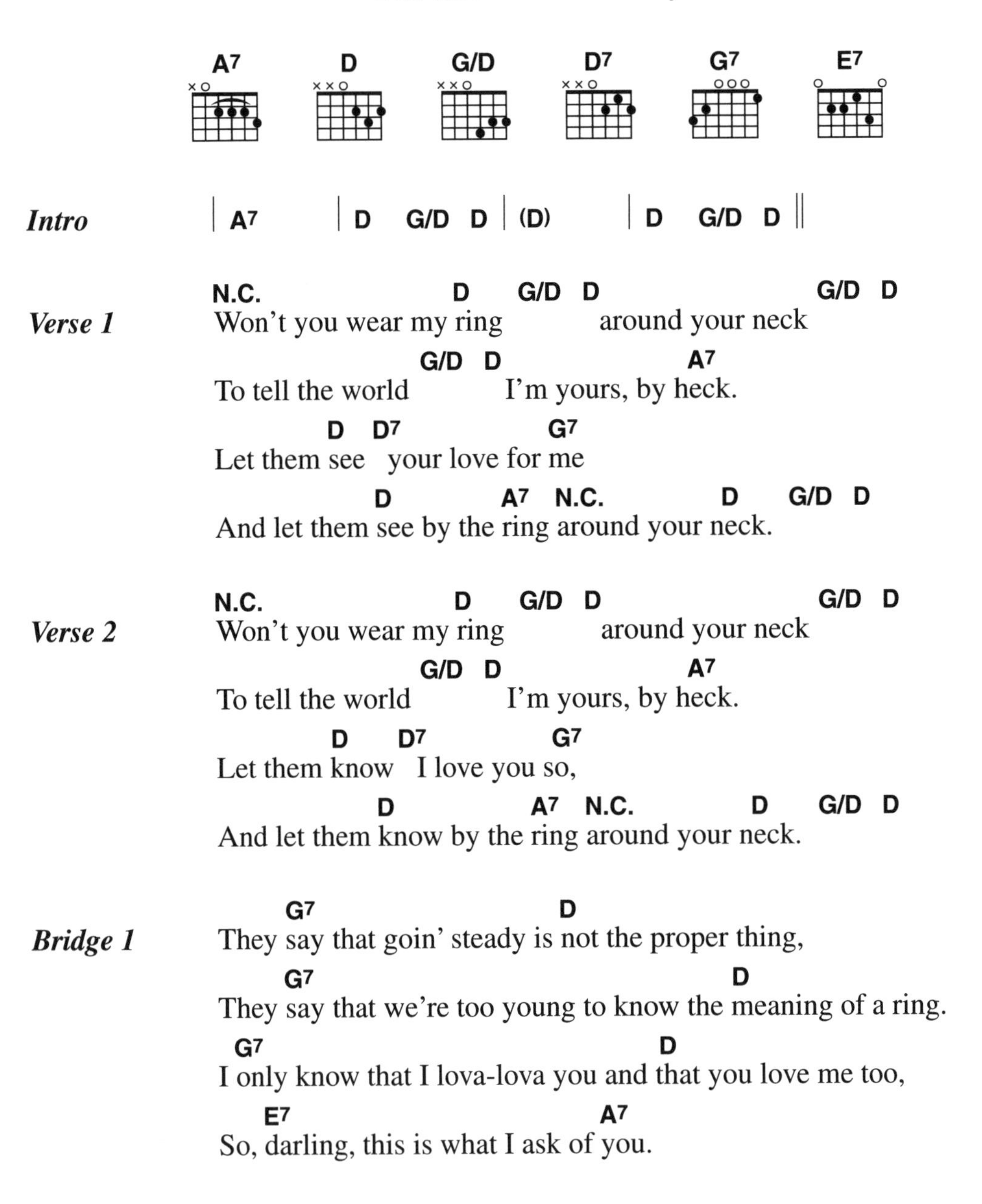

Intro | A7 | D G/D D | (D) | D G/D D ||

Verse 1

N.C. D G/D D G/D D
Won't you wear my ring around your neck
G/D D A7
To tell the world I'm yours, by heck.
D D7 G7
Let them see your love for me
D A7 N.C. D G/D D
And let them see by the ring around your neck.

Verse 2

N.C. D G/D D G/D D
Won't you wear my ring around your neck
G/D D A7
To tell the world I'm yours, by heck.
D D7 G7
Let them know I love you so,
D A7 N.C. D G/D D
And let them know by the ring around your neck.

Bridge 1

G7 D
They say that goin' steady is not the proper thing,
G7 D
They say that we're too young to know the meaning of a ring.
G7 D
I only know that I lova-lova you and that you love me too,
E7 A7
So, darling, this is what I ask of you.

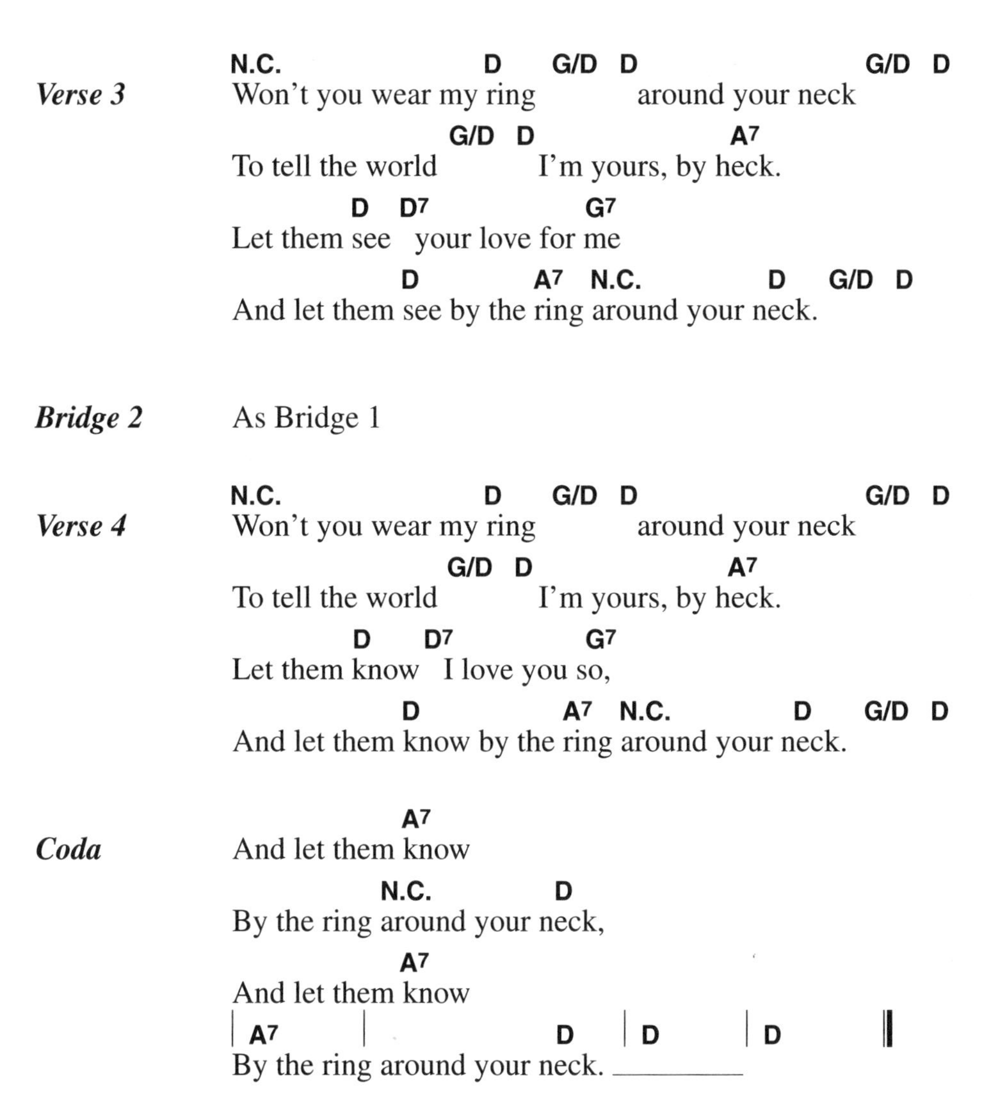

```
            N.C.              D    G/D  D                  G/D  D
Verse 3     Won't you wear my ring        around your neck
                            G/D  D               A7
            To tell the world        I'm yours, by heck.
                   D   D7             G7
            Let them see  your love for me
                     D          A7  N.C.          D   G/D  D
            And let them see by the ring around your neck.


Bridge 2    As Bridge 1

            N.C.              D    G/D  D                  G/D  D
Verse 4     Won't you wear my ring        around your neck
                            G/D  D               A7
            To tell the world        I'm yours, by heck.
                   D    D7            G7
            Let them know  I love you so,
                     D           A7  N.C.          D   G/D  D
            And let them know by the ring around your neck.

                     A7
Coda        And let them know
                     N.C.       D
            By the ring around your neck,
                     A7
            And let them know
            | A7     |            D  | D       | D        ||
            By the ring around your neck. ________
```

King Creole

Words & Music by
Jerry Leiber & Mike Stoller

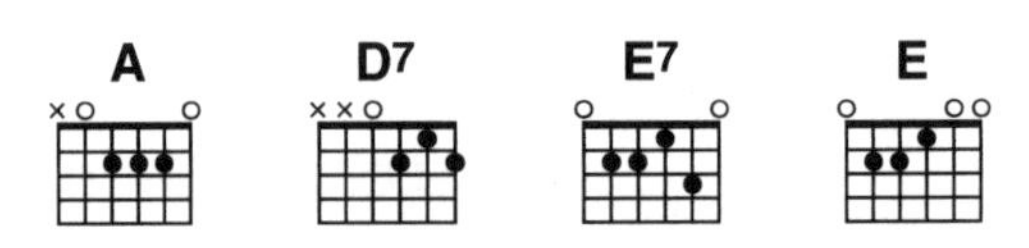

Capo first fret

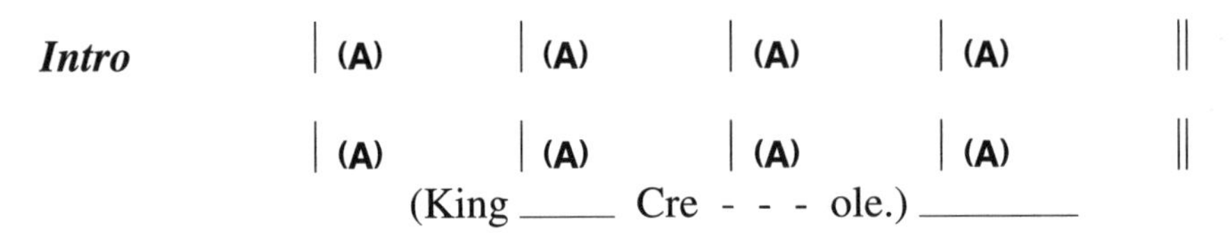

Verse 1

```
               A
There's a man in New Orleans who plays rock and roll,

He's a guitar man with a great big soul,

He lays down a beat like a ton of coal,

               N.C.
He goes by the name of King Creole.
```

Chorus 1

```
                  D7
You know he's gone, gone, gone,
                                 A
Jumping like a catfish on a pole, yeah.
                  E7                D7
You know he's gone, gone, gone,
                    A
Hip-shaking King Creole.

(King Creole, King Creole.)
```

Verse 2

```
               A
When the King starts to do it, it's as good as done:

He holds his guitar like a tommy gun,

He starts to growl from 'way down in his throat,

                 N.C.
He bends a string and that's all she wrote.
```

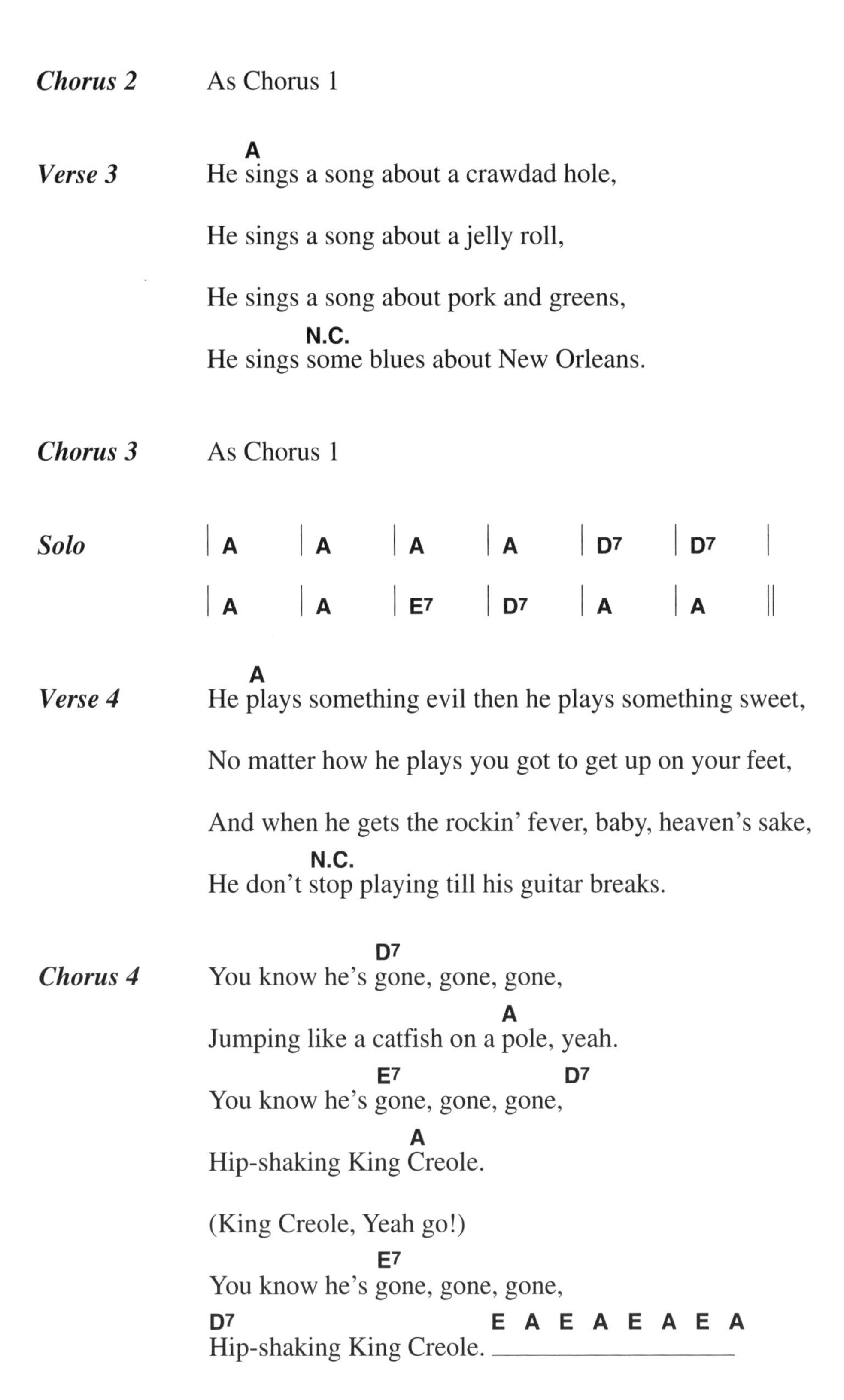

Chorus 2 As Chorus 1

Verse 3

```
   A
He sings a song about a crawdad hole,

He sings a song about a jelly roll,

He sings a song about pork and greens,

         N.C.
He sings some blues about New Orleans.
```

Chorus 3 As Chorus 1

Solo

| A | A | A | A | D7 | D7 |
| A | A | E7 | D7 | A | A ||

Verse 4

```
   A
He plays something evil then he plays something sweet,

No matter how he plays you got to get up on your feet,

And when he gets the rockin' fever, baby, heaven's sake,

          N.C.
He don't stop playing till his guitar breaks.
```

Chorus 4

```
               D7
You know he's gone, gone, gone,
                             A
Jumping like a catfish on a pole, yeah.
               E7               D7
You know he's gone, gone, gone,
                A
Hip-shaking King Creole.

(King Creole, Yeah go!)
               E7
You know he's gone, gone, gone,
D7                       E A E A E A E A
Hip-shaking King Creole. _______________
```

Hard Headed Woman

Words & Music by
Claude De Metruis

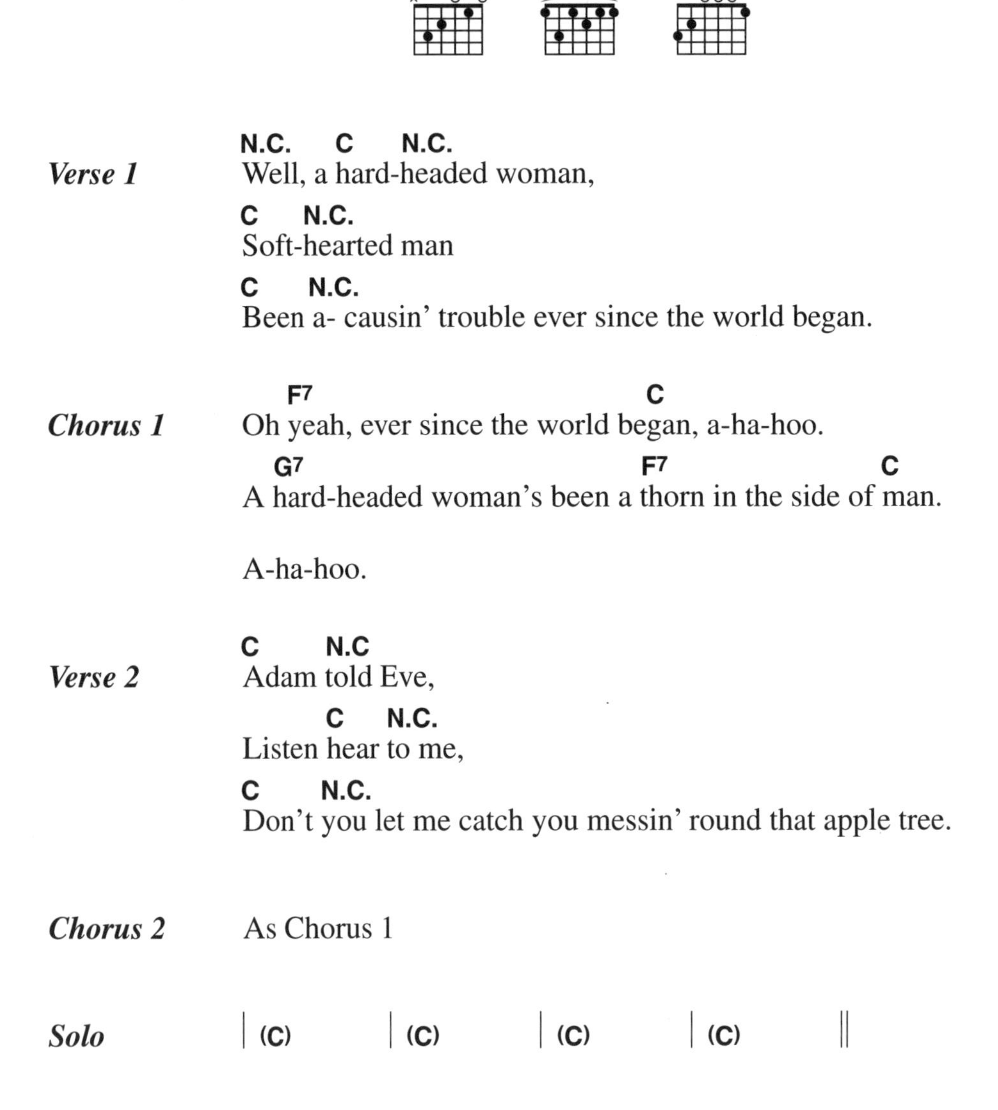

Verse 1

```
N.C.    C     N.C.
Well, a hard-headed woman,
C    N.C.
Soft-hearted man
C     N.C.
Been a- causin' trouble ever since the world began.
```

Chorus 1

```
   F7                          C
Oh yeah, ever since the world began, a-ha-hoo.
  G7                        F7               C
A hard-headed woman's been a thorn in the side of man.

A-ha-hoo.
```

Verse 2

```
C      N.C
Adam told Eve,
       C    N.C.
Listen hear to me,
C      N.C.
Don't you let me catch you messin' round that apple tree.
```

Chorus 2 As Chorus 1

Solo | (C) | (C) | (C) | (C) ||

Chorus 3 As Chorus 1

Verse 3

```
C          N.C
Samson told Delilah
C      N.C.
Loud and clear:
C      N.C.
Keep your cotton-pickin' fingers out my curly hair.
```

Chorus 4 As Chorus 1

Verse 4

```
  C      N.C
I heard about a king
            C  N.C.
Who was     doing swell
C    N.C.
Till he started playing with that evil Jezebel.
```

Chorus 5 As Chorus 1

Solo

```
| (C) | (C) | (C) | (C) | F7 | F7 |
| C   | C   | G7  | F7  | C  | C  ||
```

Verse 5

```
C  N.C
I  got a woman,
  C     N.C.
A head like a rock,
C  N.C.
If  she ever went away I'd cry around the clock.
```

Chorus 6

```
   F7                               C
Oh yeah, ever since the world began, a-ha-hoo.
  G7                              F7                 C
A hard-headed woman been a thorn in the side of man.

A-ha-hoo.
  G7                              F7         G7     C
A hard-headed woman been a thorn in the side of man. ____

A-ha-hoo.
```

One Night

Words & Music by
Dave Bartholomew, Pearl King & Anita Steiman

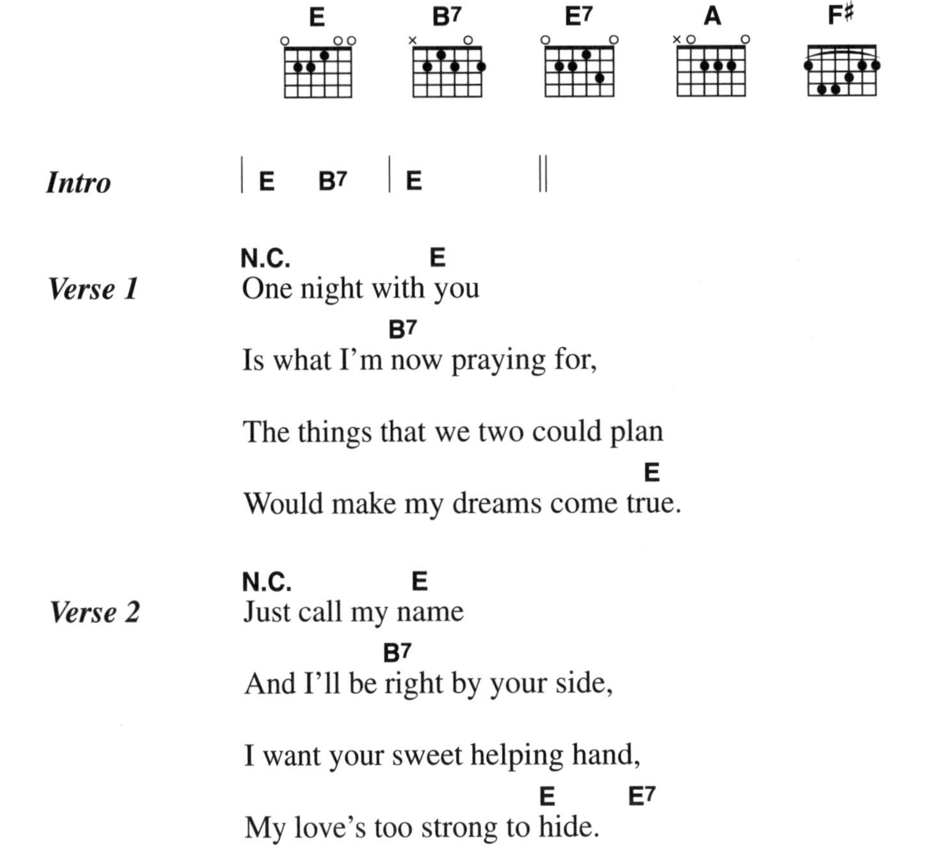

Intro | E B7 | E ||

Verse 1

```
N.C.               E
One night with you
             B7
Is what I'm now praying for,

The things that we two could plan
                                    E
Would make my dreams come true.
```

Verse 2

```
N.C.            E
Just call my name
             B7
And I'll be right by your side,

I want your sweet helping hand,
                              E       E7
My love's too strong to hide.
```

Bridge 1

```
A
  Always lived very quiet life:
E
  I ain't never did no wrong.
F♯
  Now I know that life without you
    B7    N.C.
Has been too lonely too long.
```

```
           N.C.              E
Verse 3    One night with you
                          B7
           Is what I'm now praying for,

           The things that we two could plan
                                          E       E7
           Would make my dreams come true.

           A
Bridge 2     Always lived very quiet life:
           E
             I ain't never did no wrong.
           F♯
             Now I know that life without you
               B7    N.C.
           Has been too lonely too long.

           N.C.              E
Verse 4    One night with you
                          B7
           Is what I'm now praying for,

           The things that we two could plan
           N.C.                            E    A    E    B7    E7
           Would make my dreams come true. ______
```

A Fool Such As I

Words & Music by
Bill Trader

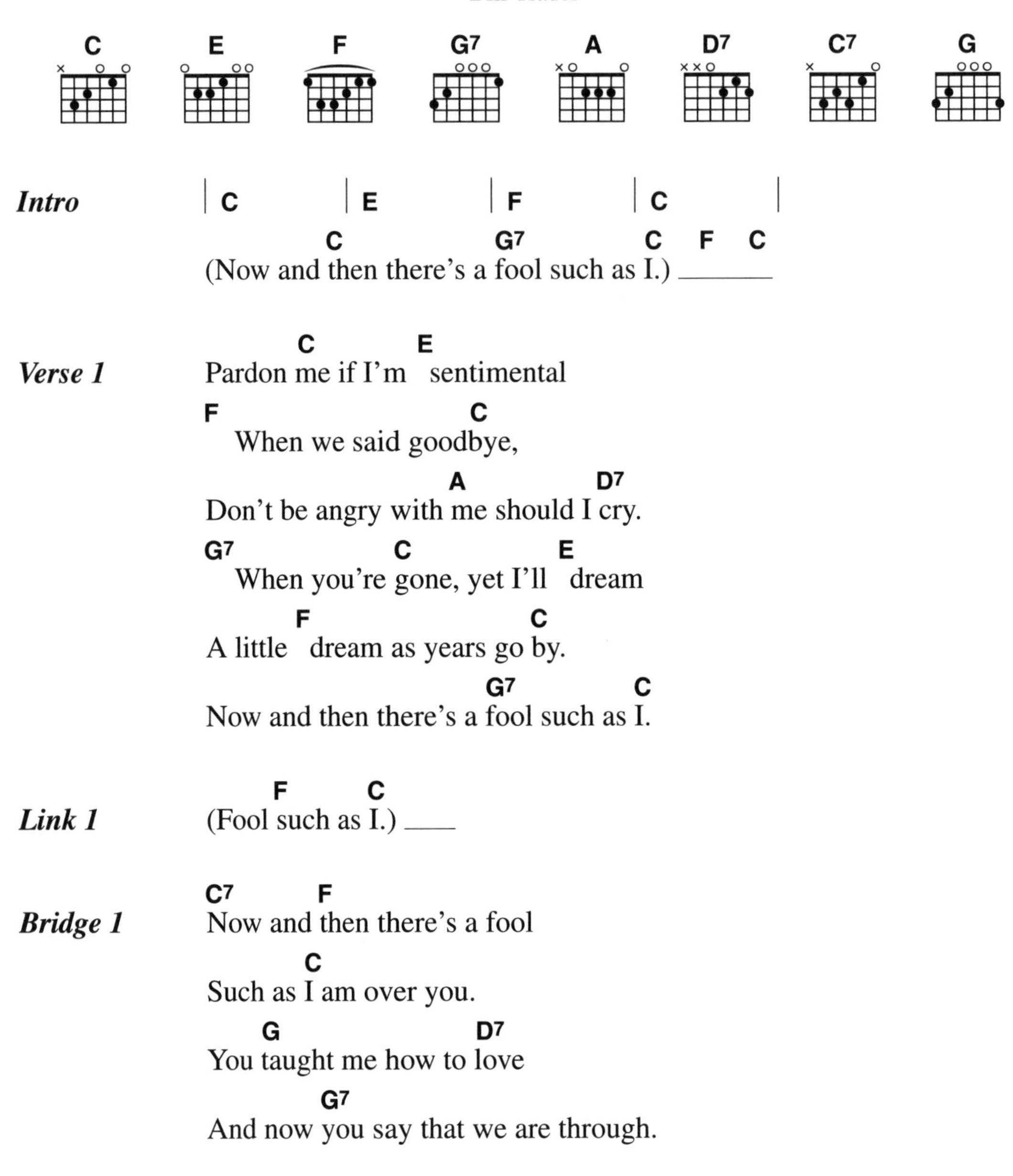

Intro

| C | E | F | C |

C G7 C F C
(Now and then there's a fool such as I.) ______

Verse 1

C E
Pardon me if I'm sentimental
F C
When we said goodbye,
A D7
Don't be angry with me should I cry.
G7 C E
When you're gone, yet I'll dream
F C
A little dream as years go by.
G7 C
Now and then there's a fool such as I.

Link 1

F C
(Fool such as I.) ____

Bridge 1

C7 F
Now and then there's a fool
C
Such as I am over you.
G D7
You taught me how to love
G7
And now you say that we are through.

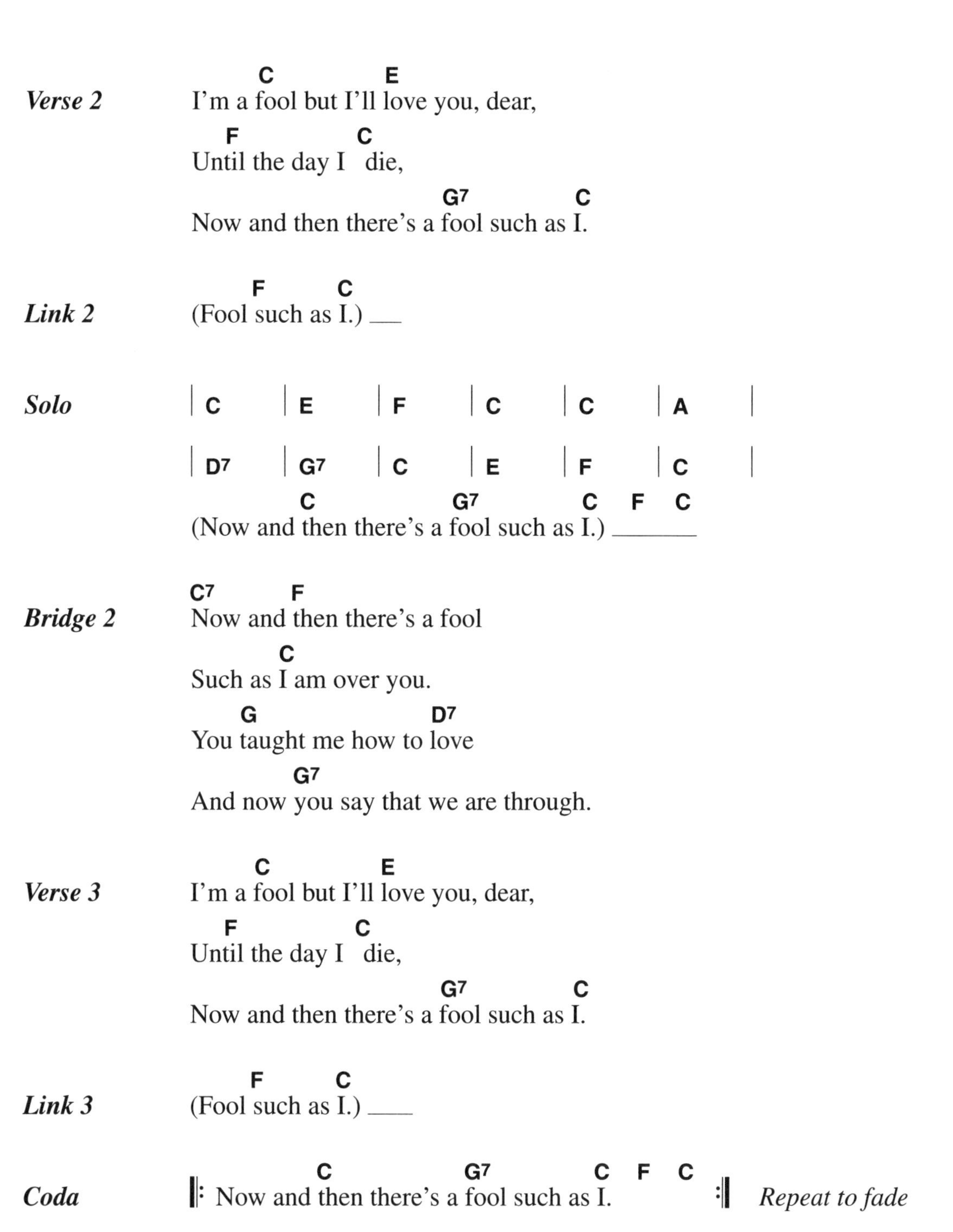

Verse 2

```
         C              E
I'm a fool but I'll love you, dear,
   F          C
Until the day I   die,
                              G7          C
Now and then there's a fool such as I.
```

Link 2

```
      F       C
(Fool such as I.) __
```

Solo

```
| C    | E    | F    | C    | C    | A    |
| D7   | G7   | C    | E    | F    | C    |
            C                G7        C   F   C
(Now and then there's a fool such as I.) ______
```

Bridge 2

```
C7          F
Now and then there's a fool
           C
Such as I am over you.
     G                 D7
You taught me how to love
            G7
And now you say that we are through.
```

Verse 3

```
         C              E
I'm a fool but I'll love you, dear,
   F          C
Until the day I   die,
                              G7          C
Now and then there's a fool such as I.
```

Link 3

```
      F       C
(Fool such as I.) __
```

Coda

```
                C                G7        C   F   C
||: Now and then there's a fool such as I.            :||
```
Repeat to fade

A Big Hunk O' Love

Words & Music by
Aaron Schroeder & Sid Wyche

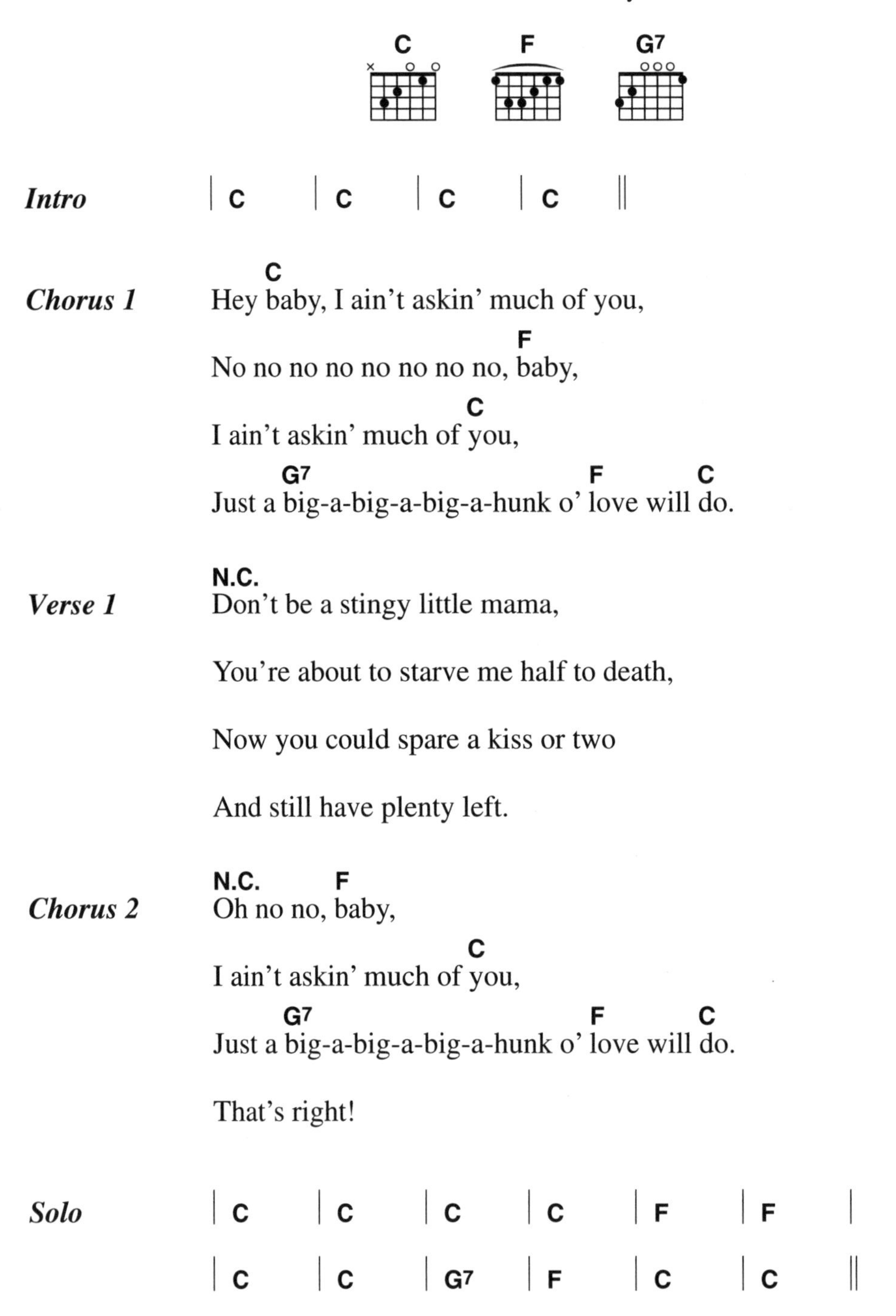

Intro | C | C | C | C ||

Chorus 1

C
Hey baby, I ain't askin' much of you,
F
No no no no no no no no, baby,
C
I ain't askin' much of you,
G7 F C
Just a big-a-big-a-big-a-hunk o' love will do.

Verse 1

N.C.
Don't be a stingy little mama,

You're about to starve me half to death,

Now you could spare a kiss or two

And still have plenty left.

Chorus 2

N.C. F
Oh no no, baby,
C
I ain't askin' much of you,
G7 F C
Just a big-a-big-a-big-a-hunk o' love will do.

That's right!

Solo | C | C | C | C | F | F |

| C | C | G7 | F | C | C ||

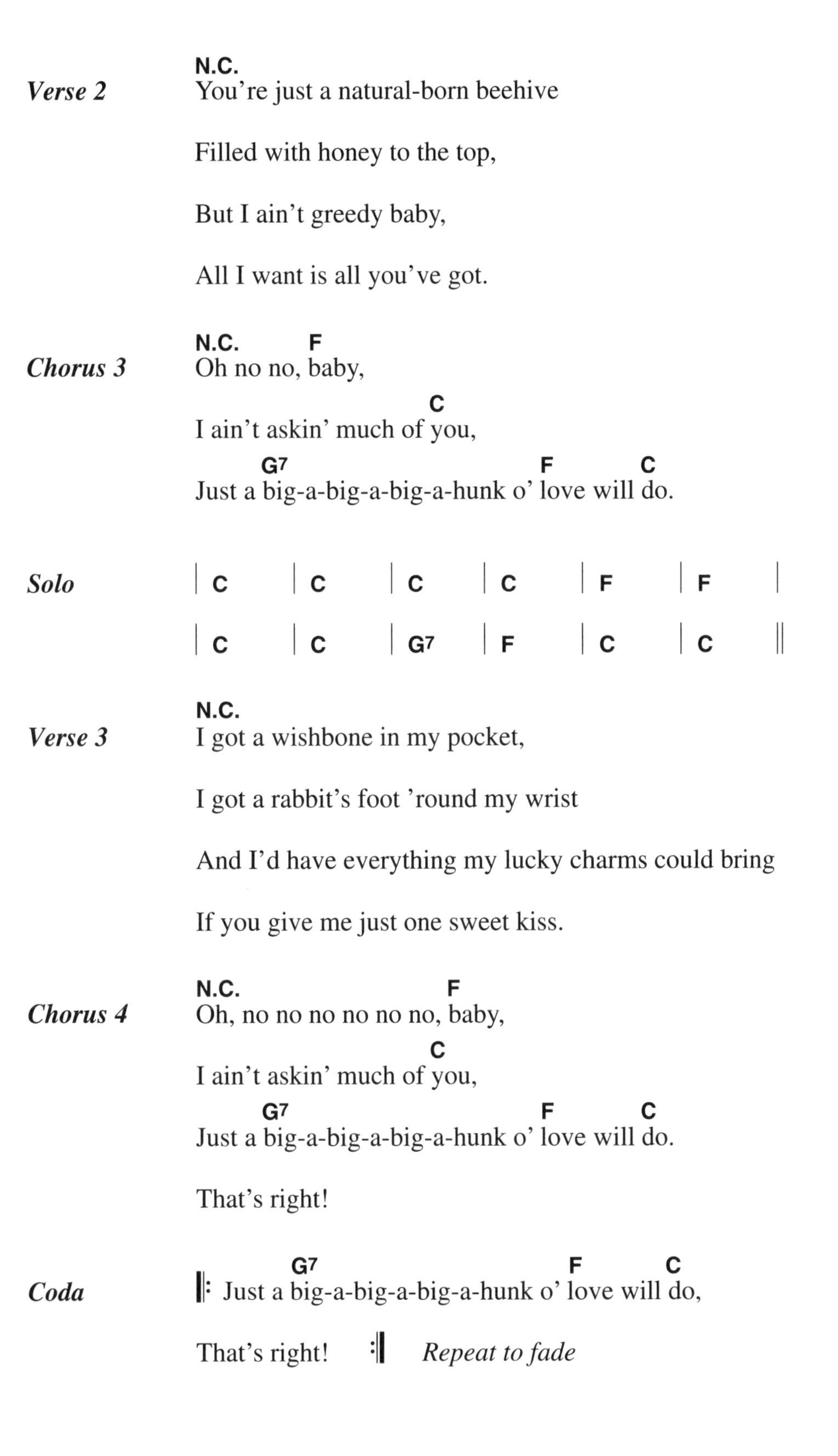

```
             N.C.
Verse 2      You're just a natural-born beehive

             Filled with honey to the top,

             But I ain't greedy baby,

             All I want is all you've got.


             N.C.        F
Chorus 3     Oh no no, baby,
                                   C
             I ain't askin' much of you,
                  G7                     F       C
             Just a big-a-big-a-big-a-hunk o' love will do.
```

Solo

C	C	C	C	F	F
C	C	G7	F	C	C ‖

```
             N.C.
Verse 3      I got a wishbone in my pocket,

             I got a rabbit's foot 'round my wrist

             And I'd have everything my lucky charms could bring

             If you give me just one sweet kiss.


             N.C.                        F
Chorus 4     Oh, no no no no no no, baby,
                                   C
             I ain't askin' much of you,
                  G7                     F       C
             Just a big-a-big-a-big-a-hunk o' love will do.

             That's right!


                     G7                     F       C
Coda         ‖: Just a big-a-big-a-big-a-hunk o' love will do,

             That's right!   :‖   Repeat to fade
```

Stuck On You

Words & Music by
Aaron Schroeder & J. Leslie McFarland

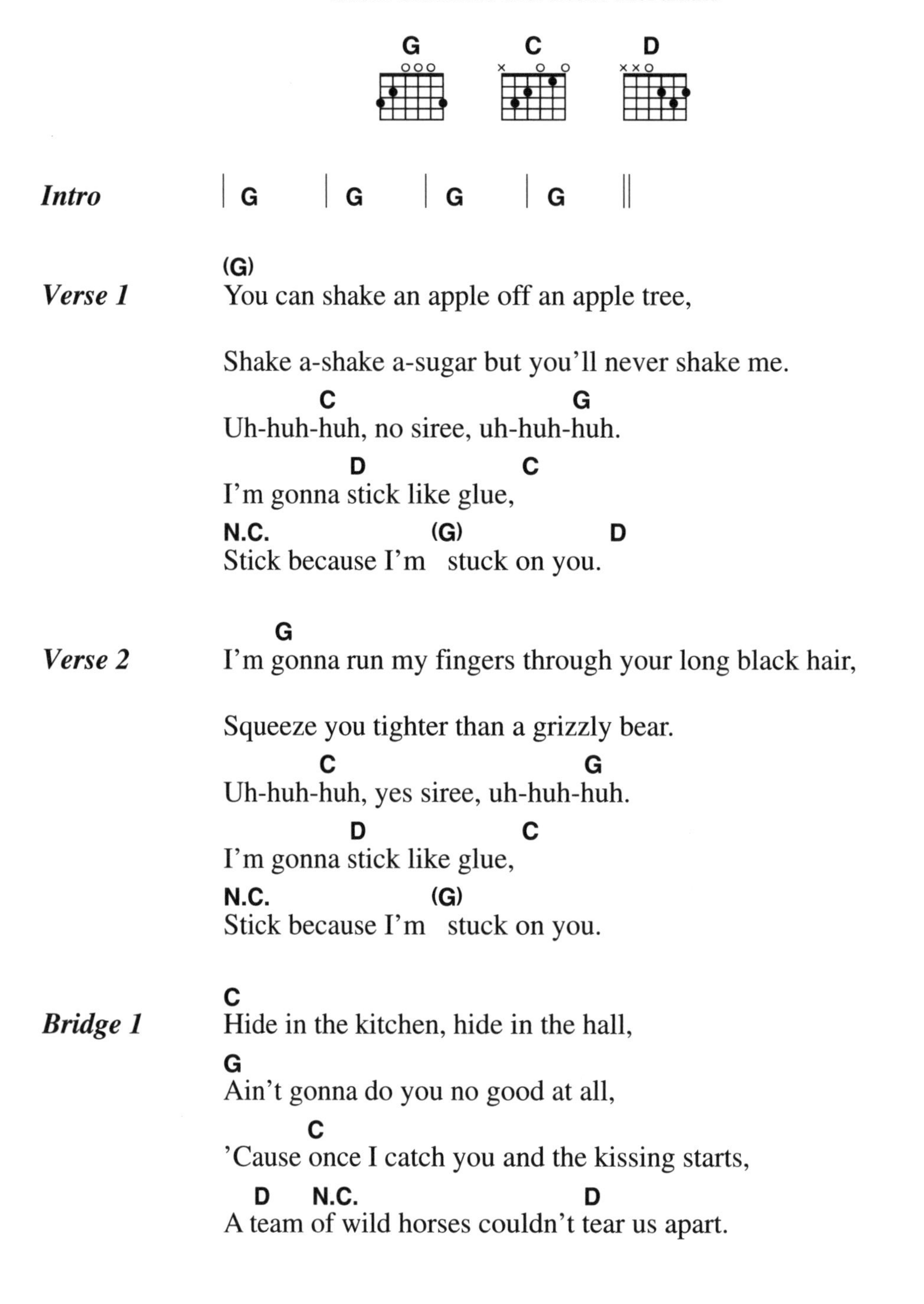

G C D

Intro | G | G | G | G ||

Verse 1

```
(G)
You can shake an apple off an apple tree,

Shake a-shake a-sugar but you'll never shake me.
           C                     G
Uh-huh-huh, no siree, uh-huh-huh.
             D                C
I'm gonna stick like glue,
N.C.                  (G)            D
Stick because I'm   stuck on you.
```

Verse 2

```
      G
I'm gonna run my fingers through your long black hair,

Squeeze you tighter than a grizzly bear.
           C                      G
Uh-huh-huh, yes siree, uh-huh-huh.
             D                C
I'm gonna stick like glue,
N.C.                  (G)
Stick because I'm   stuck on you.
```

Bridge 1

```
C
Hide in the kitchen, hide in the hall,
G
Ain't gonna do you no good at all,
         C
'Cause once I catch you and the kissing starts,
  D    N.C.                      D
A team of wild horses couldn't tear us apart.
```

```
             G
Verse 3      I thought I'd take a tiger from this Daddy's side,

             That's how love is gonna keep us tied,
                  C                        G
             Uh-huh-huh, uh-huh-huh, oh yeah.
                       D                 C
             I'm gonna stick like glue,
             N.C.                 (G)
             Stick because I'm   stuck on you.


Bridge 2     As Bridge 1

             G
Verse 4      I thought I'd take a tiger from this Daddy's side,

             That's how love is gonna keep us tied,
                  C                          G
             Uh-huh-huh, yes siree,uh-huh-huh.
                       D                 C
             I'm gonna stick like glue,
             N.C.                 (G)
             Stick because I'm   stuck on you.
                       D                 C
             I'm gonna stick like glue,
             N.C.                 (G)
             Stick because I'm   stuck on you.
```

The Girl Of My Best Friend

Words & Music by
Beverly Ross & Sam Bobrick

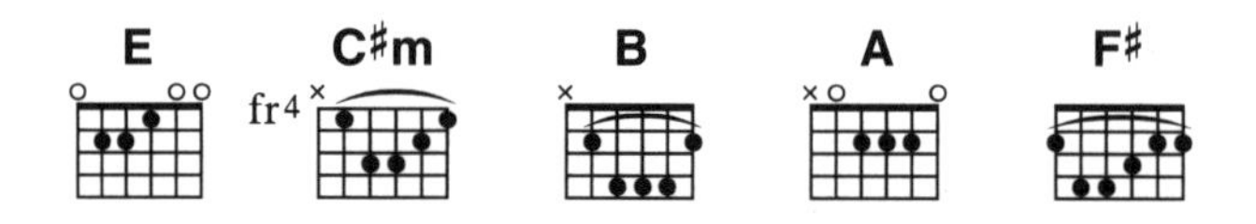

Intro

E C♯m
(Ah ah ah ah ah.)

E C♯m
(Ah ah ah ah ah.)

E C♯m
(Ah ah ah ah ah.)

E C♯m
(Ah ah ah ah ah.)

Verse 1

E C♯m
The way she walks,

E C♯m
The way she talks,

E C♯m B
How long can I pre - tend?

A B E C♯m
Oh I can't help it, I'm in love ___

A B
With the girl of my best friend.

Verse 2

E C♯m
Her lovely hair,

E C♯m
Her skin so fair,

E C♯m B
I could go on and never end.

A B E C♯m
Oh I can't help it, I'm in love ___

A B E
With the girl of my best friend.

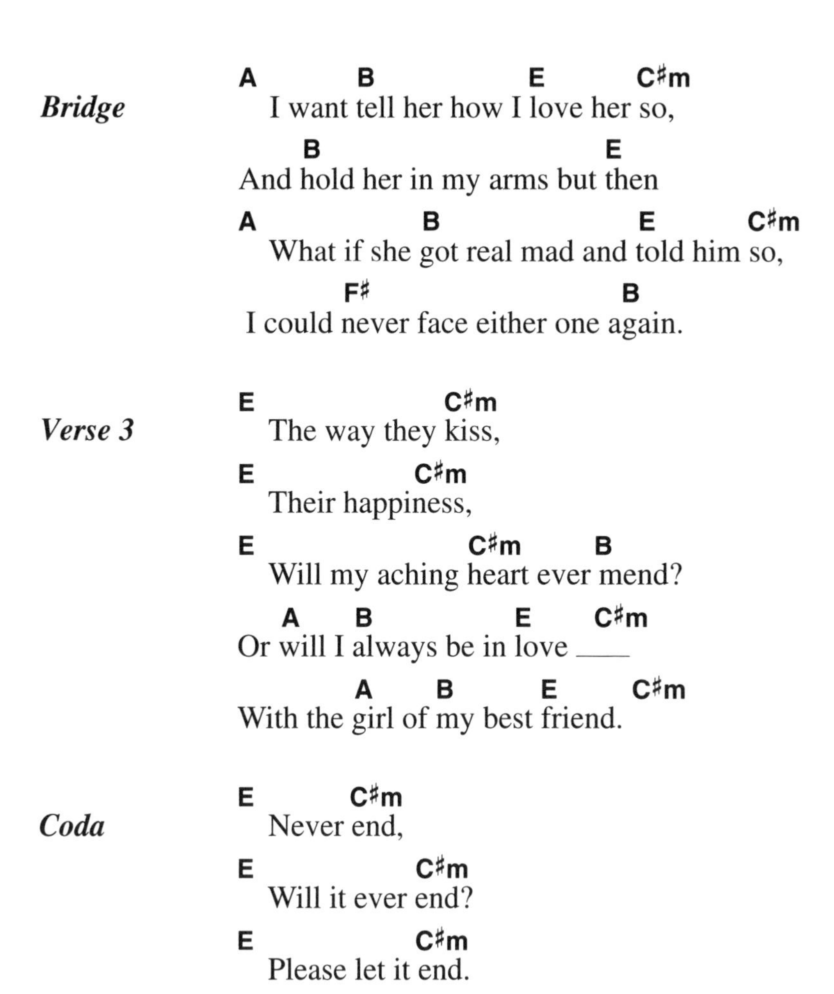

Bridge

A B E C♯m
I want tell her how I love her so,

B E
And hold her in my arms but then

A B E C♯m
What if she got real mad and told him so,

F♯ B
I could never face either one again.

Verse 3

E C♯m
The way they kiss,

E C♯m
Their happiness,

E C♯m B
Will my aching heart ever mend?

A B E C♯m
Or will I always be in love ___

A B E C♯m
With the girl of my best friend.

Coda

E C♯m
Never end,

E C♯m
Will it ever end?

E C♯m
Please let it end.

It's Now Or Never

Original Italian Words by Giovanni Capurro
Music by E. di Capua
English Words by Aaron Schroeder & Wally Gold

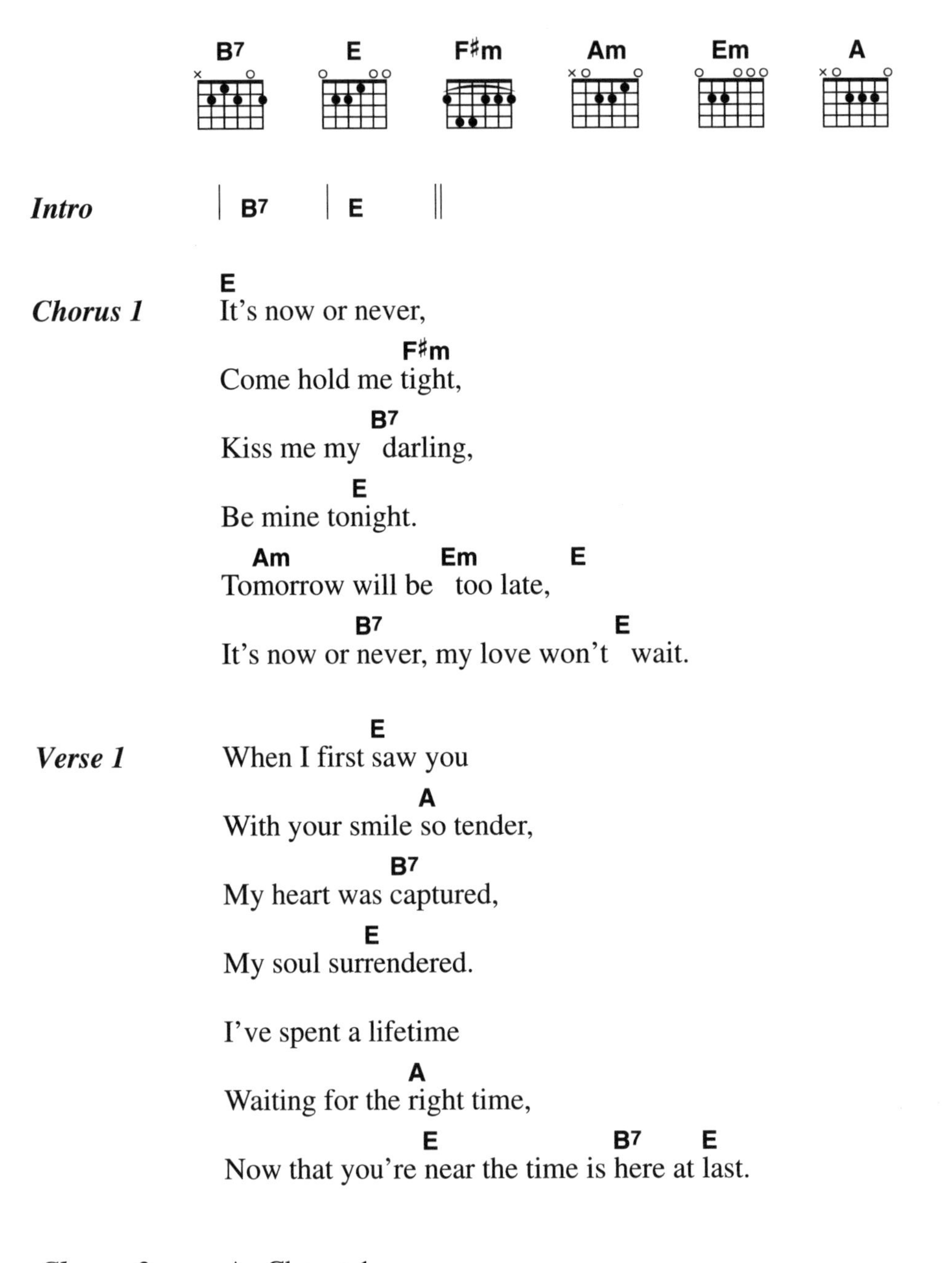

Intro | B7 | E ||

Chorus 1

E
It's now or never,
F♯m
Come hold me tight,
B7
Kiss me my darling,
E
Be mine tonight.
Am Em E
Tomorrow will be too late,
B7 E
It's now or never, my love won't wait.

Verse 1

E
When I first saw you
A
With your smile so tender,
B7
My heart was captured,
E
My soul surrendered.

I've spent a lifetime
A
Waiting for the right time,
E B7 E
Now that you're near the time is here at last.

Chorus 2 As Chorus 1

Verse 2

E
Just like a willow

A
We would cry an ocean,

B7
If we lost true love

E
And sweet devotion.

Your lips excite me,

A
Let your arms invite me,

E B7 E
For who knows when we'll meet again this way.

Chorus 3

N.C. F♯m
It's now or never,

F♯m
Come hold me tight,

B7
Kiss me my darling,

E
Be mine tonight.

Am Em E
Tomorrow will be too late,

B7 E
It's now or never, my love won't wait.

B7 E
It's now or never, my love won't wait.

N.C. E
It's now or never, my love won't wait.

B7 E
It's now or never, my love won't wait.

Are You Lonesome Tonight?

Words & Music by
Roy Turk & Lou Handman

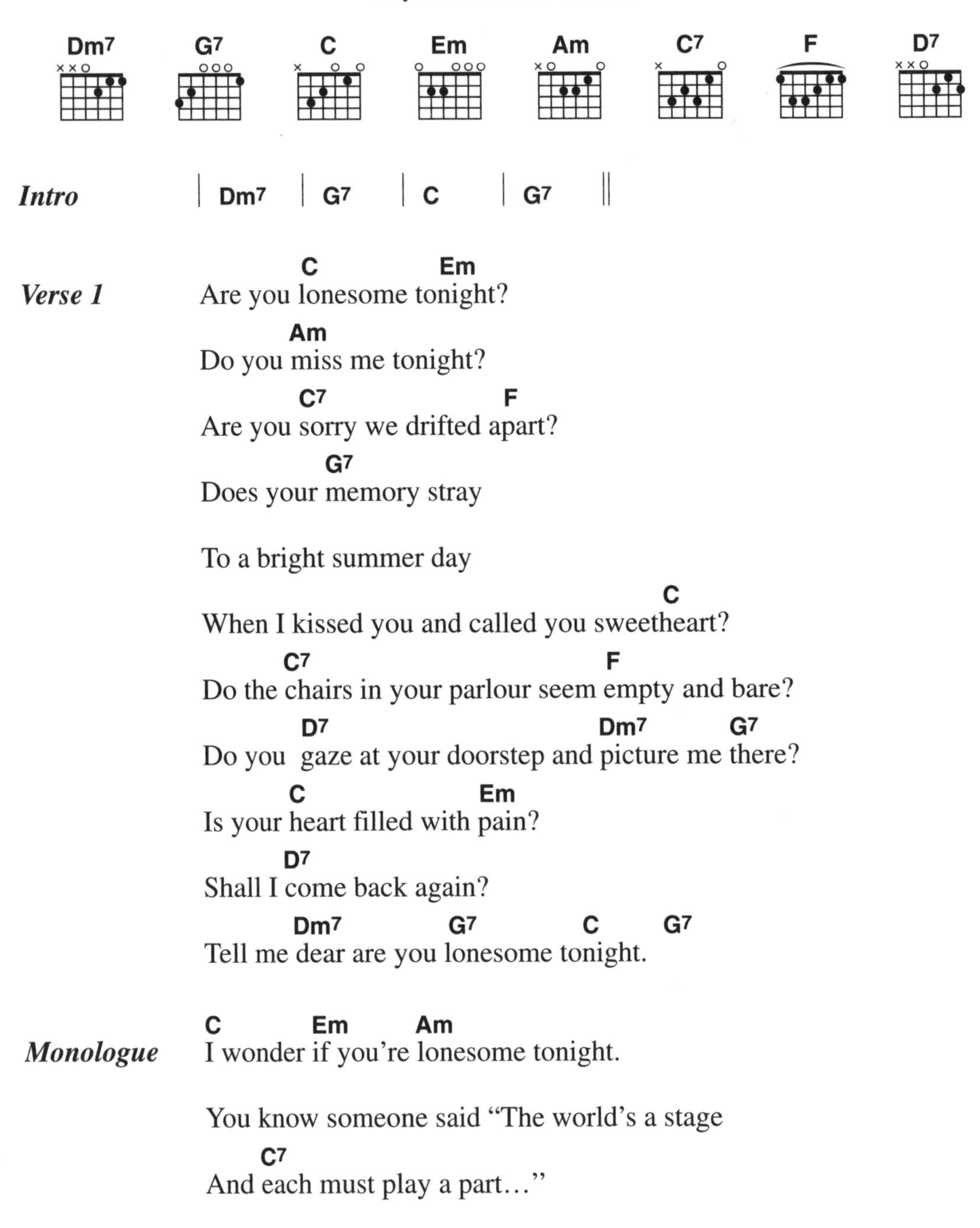

Intro | Dm7 | G7 | C | G7 ||

Verse 1

C Em
Are you lonesome tonight?
Am
Do you miss me tonight?
C7 F
Are you sorry we drifted apart?
G7
Does your memory stray

To a bright summer day
C
When I kissed you and called you sweetheart?
C7 F
Do the chairs in your parlour seem empty and bare?
D7 Dm7 G7
Do you gaze at your doorstep and picture me there?
C Em
Is your heart filled with pain?
D7
Shall I come back again?
Dm7 G7 C G7
Tell me dear are you lonesome tonight.

Monologue

C Em Am
I wonder if you're lonesome tonight.

You know someone said "The world's a stage
C7
And each must play a part…"

cont.

F
Fate had me playing in love with you as my sweetheart.

Act One was where we met,

G7
I loved you at first glance.

You read your lines so cleverly and never missed a cue.

Then came Act Two:

You seemed to change, you acted strange

C
And why I've never known.

C7
Honey you lied when you said you loved me

F
And I had no cause to doubt you,

D7
But I'd rather go on hearing your lies

Dm7 G7
Than to go on living without you.

C Em
Now the stage is bare and I'm standing there

D7
With emptiness all around.

Dm7
And if you won't come back to me

G7 C G7
Then they can bring the curtain down.

Coda

C Em
Is your heart filled with pain?

D7
Shall I come back again?

Dm7 G7 C
Tell me dear are you lonesome tonight?

Wooden Heart

Words & Music by
Fred Wise, Ben Weisman, Kay Twomey & Bert Kaempfert

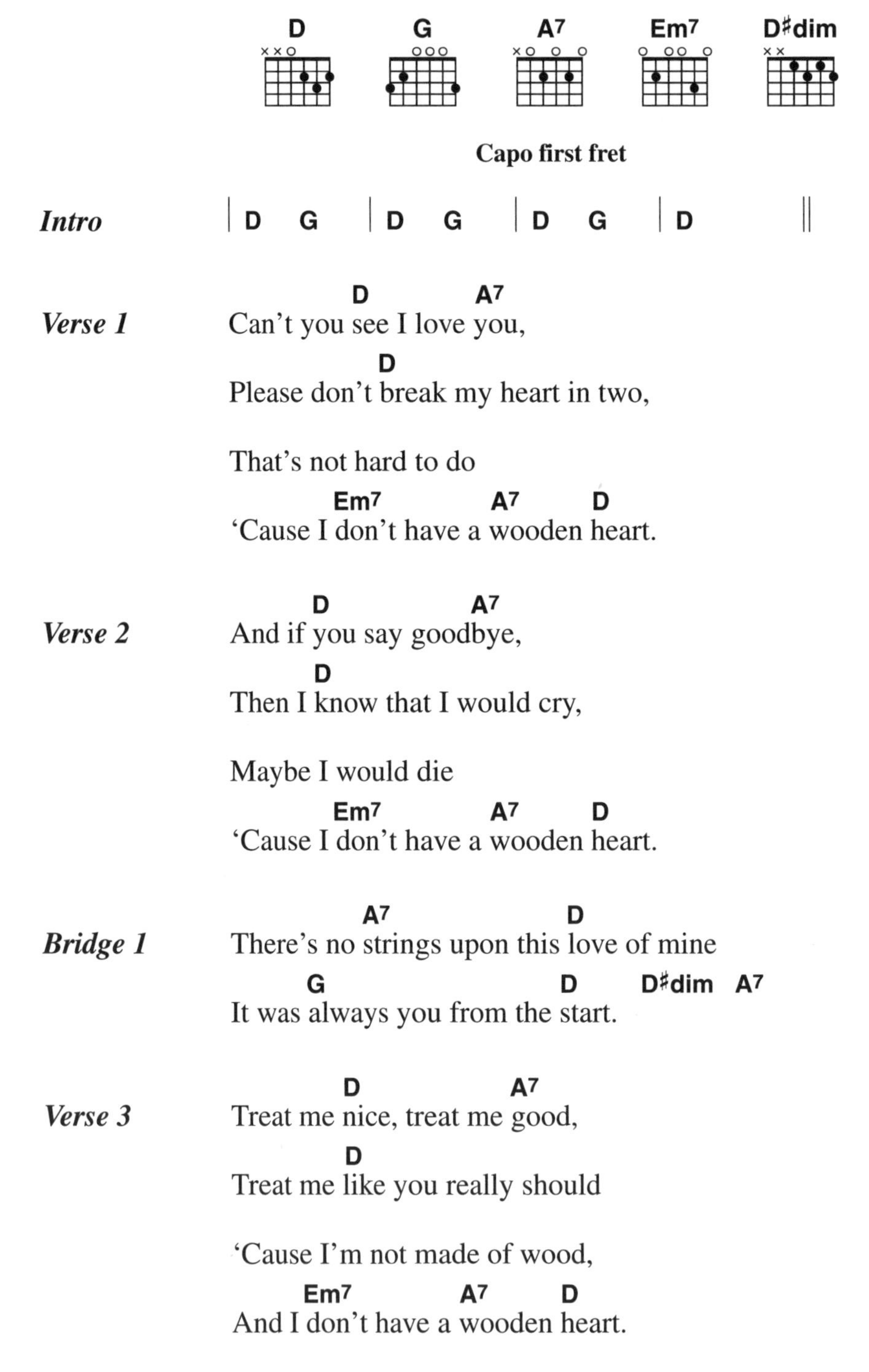

D G A7 Em7 D♯dim

Capo first fret

Intro | D G | D G | D G | D ||

Verse 1
D A7
Can't you see I love you,
D
Please don't break my heart in two,

That's not hard to do
Em7 A7 D
'Cause I don't have a wooden heart.

Verse 2
D A7
And if you say goodbye,
D
Then I know that I would cry,

Maybe I would die
Em7 A7 D
'Cause I don't have a wooden heart.

Bridge 1
A7 D
There's no strings upon this love of mine
G D D♯dim A7
It was always you from the start.

Verse 3
D A7
Treat me nice, treat me good,
D
Treat me like you really should

'Cause I'm not made of wood,
Em7 A7 D
And I don't have a wooden heart.

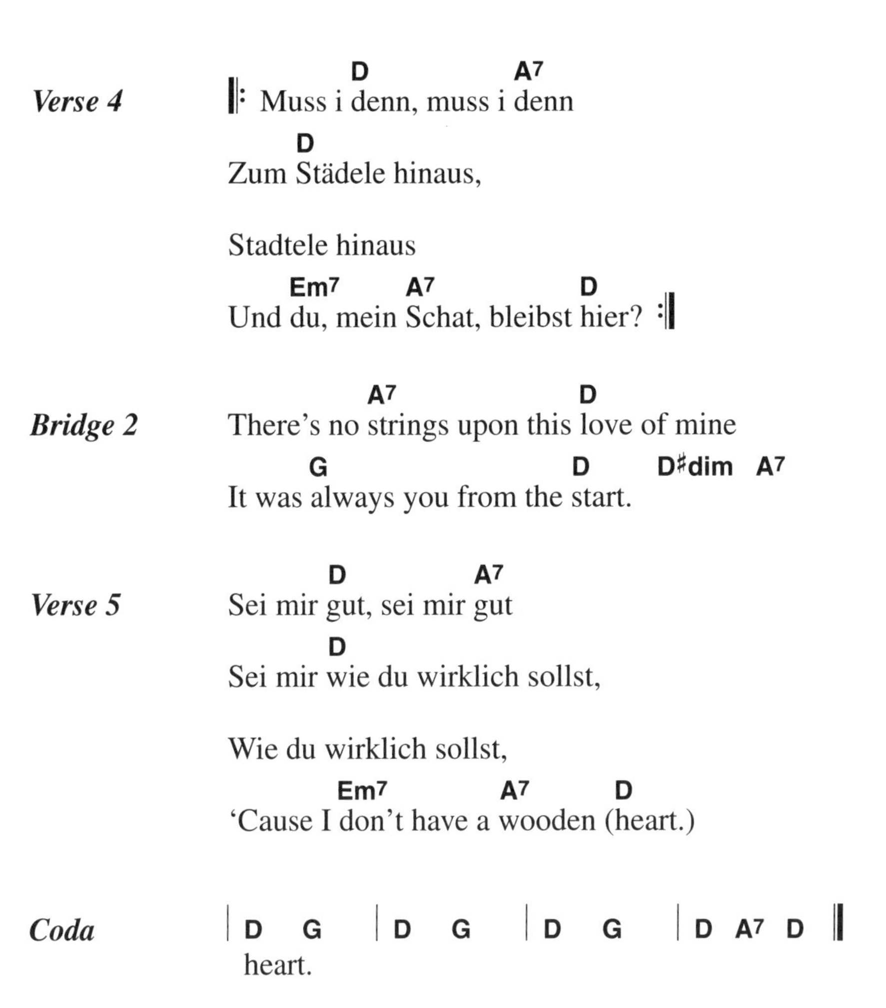

Verse 4

D A7
𝄆 Muss i denn, muss i denn

D
Zum Städele hinaus,

Stadtele hinaus

Em7 A7 D
Und du, mein Schat, bleibst hier? 𝄇

Bridge 2

A7 D
There's no strings upon this love of mine

G D D♯dim A7
It was always you from the start.

Verse 5

D A7
Sei mir gut, sei mir gut

D
Sei mir wie du wirklich sollst,

Wie du wirklich sollst,

Em7 A7 D
'Cause I don't have a wooden (heart.)

Coda

| D G | D G | D G | D A7 D ||
heart.

Surrender

Original Italian Words by G.B. De Curtis
Music by E. De Curtis
English Words & Adaptation by Doc Pomus & Mort Shuman

Capo first fret

Intro ‖: Dm Daug | Dm6 Daug :‖ *Play 3 times*

Verse

```
Dm  Daug       Dm6       Daug       Dm
     When we kiss my heart's on fire
Gm                              Dm
   Burning with a strange desire,
Gm                            Dm
   And I know each time I   kiss you
A7                              Dm
   That your heart's on fire too.
```

Chorus

```
N.C.                            Em7
So, my darling, please surrender
A7                                 D6
   All your love so warm and tender,
                          Em7
Let me hold you in my arms, dear,
A7                                    D6
   While the moon shines bright above.
                             Em7
All the stars will tell the story
A7           F♯                 Bm
   Of our love and all its glory,
Gm                               Dm
   Let us take this night of   magic
A7                             Dm
   And make it a night of love.
```

```
            N.C.                    Em7
Coda        Won't you please surrender to me
            A7                          D6
              Your lips, your arms, your heart, dear.
            Gm              Dm    A7  N.C.
              Be mine forever,        be mine to - (night.)

            | Dm    Daug  | Dm6   Daug |
            - night.

            ||: Dm    Daug  | Dm6   Daug :||  Repeat to fade
```

(Marie's The Name) His Latest Flame

Words & Music by
Doc Pomus & Mort Shuman

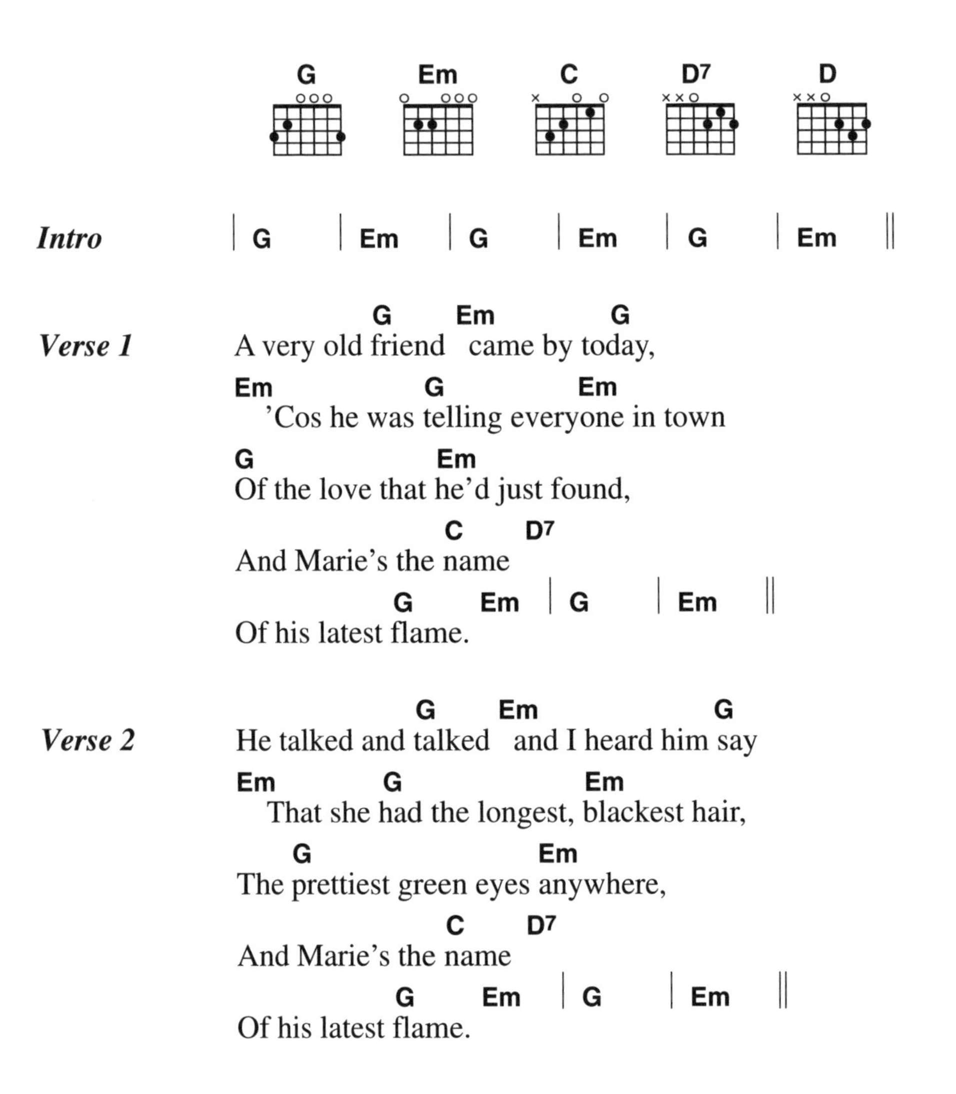

Intro | G | Em | G | Em | G | Em ||

Verse 1

```
               G       Em            G
A very old friend   came by today,
Em              G          Em
   'Cos he was telling everyone in town
G                 Em
Of the love that he'd just found,
                C       D7
And Marie's the name
             G       Em   | G       | Em      ||
Of his latest flame.
```

Verse 2

```
                 G       Em                G
He talked and talked   and I heard him say
Em          G                     Em
   That she had the longest, blackest hair,
    G                        Em
The prettiest green eyes anywhere,
                C       D7
And Marie's the name
             G       Em   | G       | Em      ||
Of his latest flame.
```

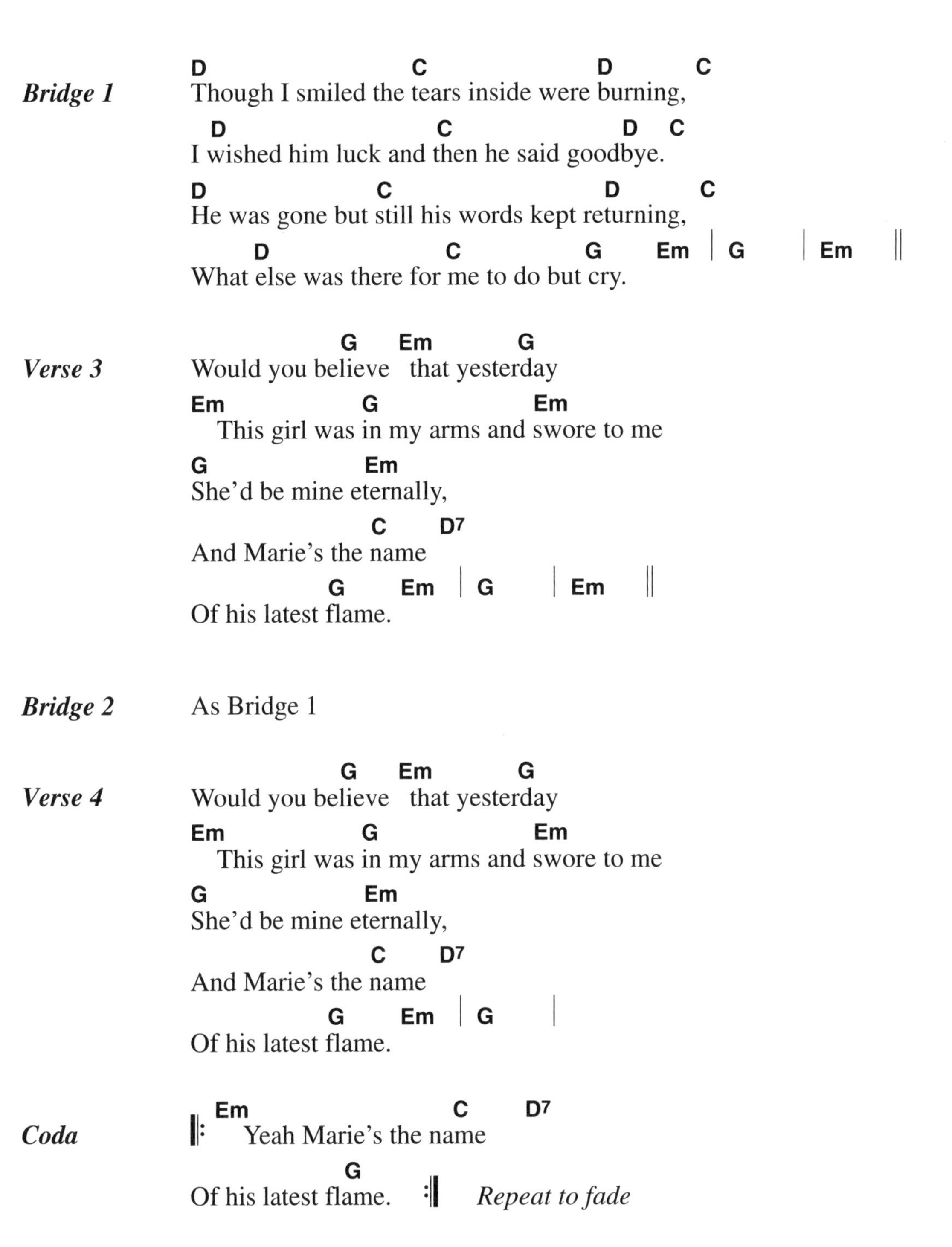

```
              D                 C              D       C
Bridge 1      Though I smiled the tears inside were burning,
                D                 C                D   C
              I wished him luck and then he said goodbye.
              D              C                  D       C
              He was gone but still his words kept returning,
                   D                C          G     Em | G     | Em  ||
              What else was there for me to do but cry.

                                G    Em      G
Verse 3       Would you believe   that yesterday
              Em              G            Em
                 This girl was in my arms and swore to me
              G              Em
              She'd be mine eternally,
                               C     D7
              And Marie's the name
                               G    Em | G     | Em  ||
              Of his latest flame.

Bridge 2      As Bridge 1

                                G    Em      G
Verse 4       Would you believe   that yesterday
              Em              G            Em
                 This girl was in my arms and swore to me
              G              Em
              She'd be mine eternally,
                               C     D7
              And Marie's the name
                               G    Em | G     |
              Of his latest flame.

                Em                  C     D7
Coda          ||:  Yeah Marie's the name
                            G
              Of his latest flame.   :||   Repeat to fade
```

Can't Help Falling In Love

Words & Music by
George David Weiss, Hugo Peretti & Luigi Creatore

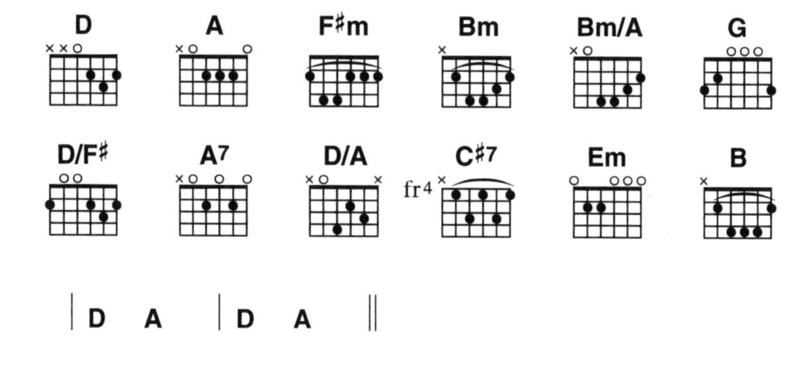

Intro | D A | D A ||

Verse 1

D F♯m Bm
Wise men say

Bm/A G D/F♯ A7
Only fools rush in

G A Bm
But I can't help

G D/A A7 D
Falling in love with you.

Verse 2

D F♯m Bm
Shall I stay,

Bm/A G D/F♯ A7
Would it be a sin,

G A Bm G D/A A7 D
If I can't help falling in love with you?

Bridge 1

F♯m C♯7
Like a river flows

F♯m C♯7
Surely to the sea,

F♯m C♯7
Darling so it goes:

F♯m B Em A7
Some things are meant to be.

```
            D      F♯m  Bm
Verse 3     Take my    hand,
            Bm/A    G      D/F♯  A7
            Take my whole life    too,
                G   A     Bm  G          D/A   A7   D
            For I     can't help falling in love  with you.

            F♯m           C♯7
Bridge 2    Like a river flows
            F♯m             C♯7
             Surely to the sea,
            F♯m            C♯7
            Darling so it goes:
            F♯m            B                Em    A7
            Some things   are meant to be.

            D       F♯m  Bm
Verse 4     Take  my    hand,
            Bm/A     G      D/F♯  A7
            Take my whole life   too,
                G    A     Bm  G          D/A   A7   D
            For I     can't help falling in love  with you,
                G    A     Bm  G          D/A   A7   D
            For I     can't help falling in love  with you.
```

Good Luck Charm

Words & Music by
Aaron Schroeder & Wally Gold

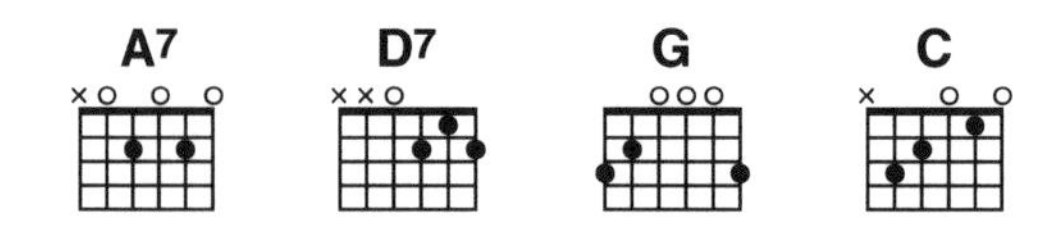

Intro

```
          A7              D7              G
Ah-huh-huh, ah-huh-huh, ah-huh-huh, oh yeah.
```

Verse 1

```
G                            C
Don't wanna four leaf clover,
G                                 D7
Don't wanna an old horse shoe.
G                           C
Want your kiss 'cause I just can't miss
         D7                       G
With a good luck charm like you.
```

Chorus 1

```
N.C.           D7                                         G
C'mon and be my little good luck charm, ah-huh-huh,

You sweet delight.
          D7
I wanna good luck charm

A-hanging on my arm
   A7                  D7                 G
To have (to have,) to hold, (to hold,) tonight.
```

Verse 2

```
G                        C
Don't wanna silver dollar,
G                      D7
Rabbit's foot on a string,
     G                          C
My happiness and your warm caress
     D7                  G
No rabbit's foot can bring.
```

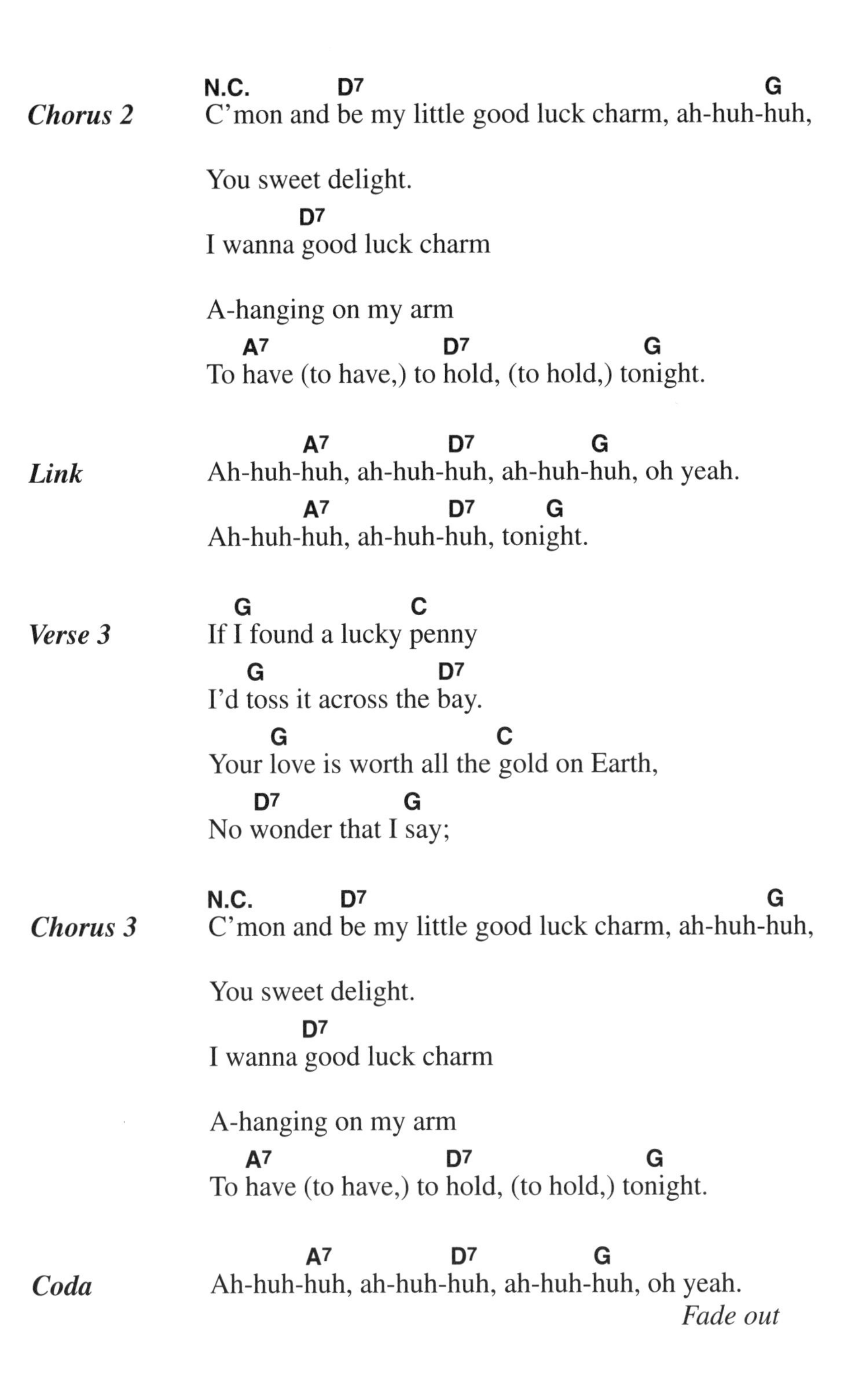

Chorus 2

N.C. D7 G
C'mon and be my little good luck charm, ah-huh-huh,

You sweet delight.

D7
I wanna good luck charm

A-hanging on my arm

A7 D7 G
To have (to have,) to hold, (to hold,) tonight.

Link

A7 D7 G
Ah-huh-huh, ah-huh-huh, ah-huh-huh, oh yeah.

A7 D7 G
Ah-huh-huh, ah-huh-huh, tonight.

Verse 3

G C
If I found a lucky penny

G D7
I'd toss it across the bay.

G C
Your love is worth all the gold on Earth,

D7 G
No wonder that I say;

Chorus 3

N.C. D7 G
C'mon and be my little good luck charm, ah-huh-huh,

You sweet delight.

D7
I wanna good luck charm

A-hanging on my arm

A7 D7 G
To have (to have,) to hold, (to hold,) tonight.

Coda

A7 D7 G
Ah-huh-huh, ah-huh-huh, ah-huh-huh, oh yeah.

Fade out

She's Not You

Words & Music by
Jerry Leiber, Mike Stoller & Doc Pomus

F C7 B♭ C A F7 A7

Verse 1

N.C. F C7
Her hair is soft and her eyes are oh so blue,
B♭ C7
She's all the things a girl should be,
F C
But she's not you.

Verse 2

N.C. F C7
She knows just how to make me laugh when I feel blue.
B♭ C7
She's ev'rything a man could want,
F B♭ F
But she's not you.

Bridge 1

A
And when we're dancing
F7
It almost feels the same,
B♭
I've got to stop myself from
A7 N.C.
Whisp'ring your name.

Verse 3

N.C. F C7
She even kisses me like you used to do.
B♭ C7
And it's just breaking my heart
F C
'Cause she's not you.

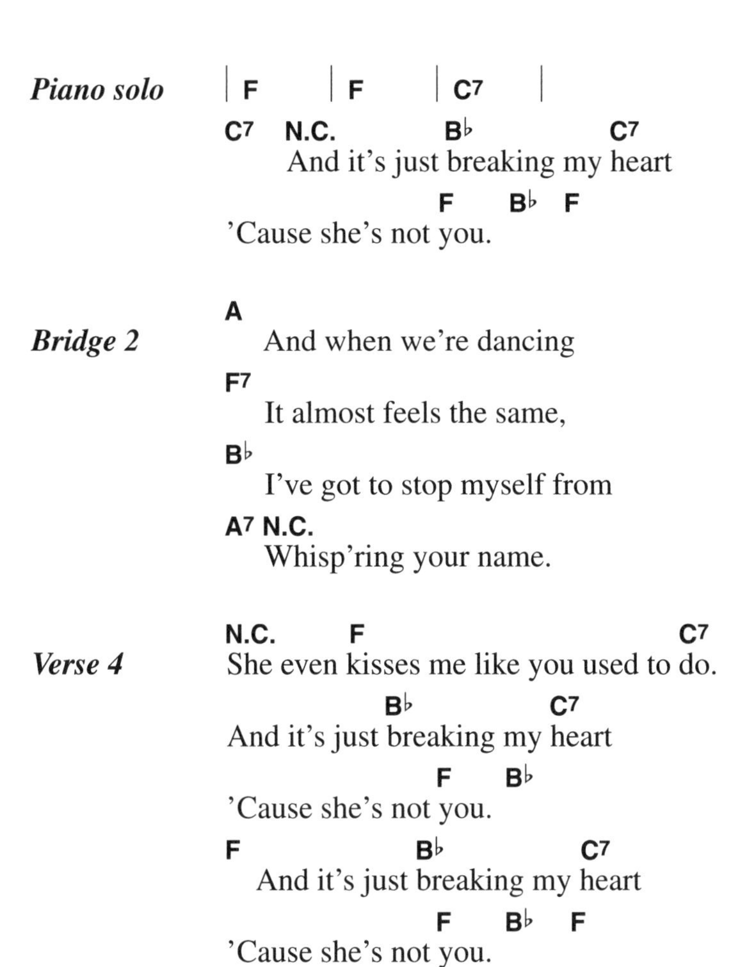

Piano solo | F | F | C7 |

C7 N.C. Bb C7
And it's just breaking my heart
F Bb F
'Cause she's not you.

Bridge 2

A
And when we're dancing
F7
It almost feels the same,
Bb
I've got to stop myself from
A7 N.C.
Whisp'ring your name.

Verse 4

N.C. F C7
She even kisses me like you used to do.
Bb C7
And it's just breaking my heart
F Bb
'Cause she's not you.
F Bb C7
And it's just breaking my heart
F Bb F
'Cause she's not you.

Return To Sender

Words & Music by
Otis Blackwell & Winfield Scott

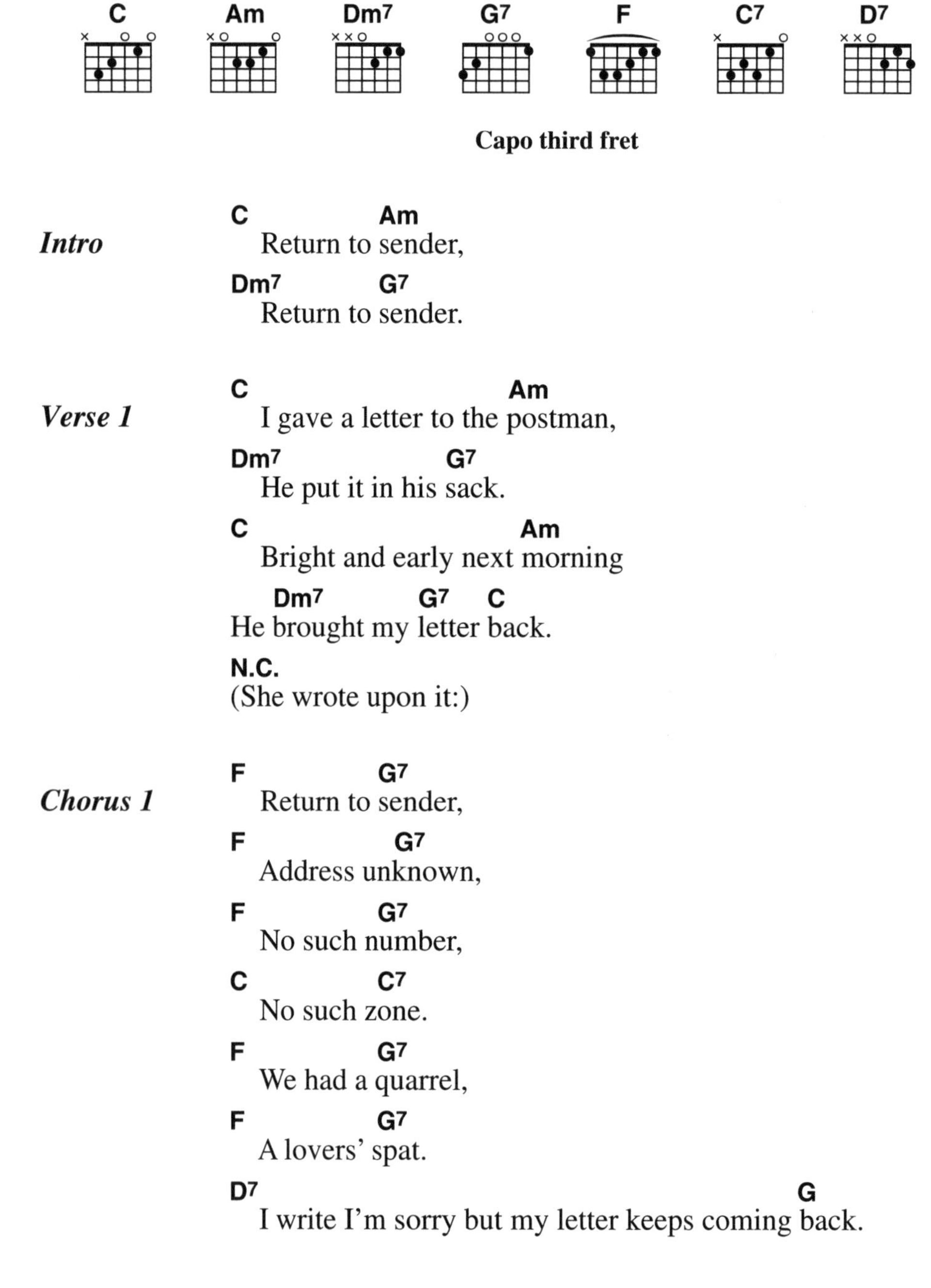

Capo third fret

Intro

C Am
Return to sender,
Dm7 G7
Return to sender.

Verse 1

C Am
I gave a letter to the postman,
Dm7 G7
He put it in his sack.
C Am
Bright and early next morning
Dm7 G7 C
He brought my letter back.
N.C.
(She wrote upon it:)

Chorus 1

F G7
Return to sender,
F G7
Address unknown,
F G7
No such number,
C C7
No such zone.
F G7
We had a quarrel,
F G7
A lovers' spat.
D7 G
I write I'm sorry but my letter keeps coming back.

Verse 2

```
C                                Am
   So then I dropped it in the mailbox,
Dm7                G7
And sent it special D
C                          Am
   Bright and early next morning
   Dm7           G7    C
It came right back to me.
N.C.
(She wrote upon it:)
```

Chorus 2

```
F              G7
   Return to sender,
F                G7
   Address unknown,
F              G7
   No such person,
C              C7
   No such zone.
```

Bridge

```
F
   This time I'm gonna take it myself
      C
And put it right in her hand,
      D7
And if it comes back the very next day
G
Then I'll understand.
N.C.
(The writing in it.)
```

Chorus 3

```
F              G7
   Return to sender,
F                G7
   Address unknown,
F              G7
   No such number,
C              C7
   No such zone.
```

Chorus 4

```
   F             G7
|: Return to sender. :|   Repeat to fade
```

(You're The) Devil In Disguise

Words & Music by
Bill Giant, Bernie Baum & Florence Kaye

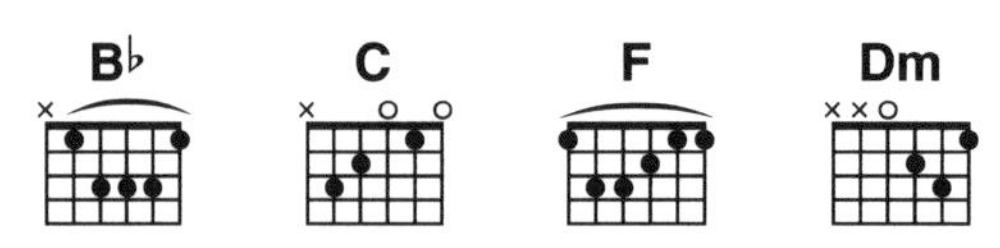

Intro | B♭ C | F ||

Pre-chorus 1
```
         F
You look like an angel, walk like an angel,
B♭                               C
Talk like an angel, but I got wise.
```

Chorus 1
```
N.C.                        F
You're the devil in disguise,
                Dm
Oh yes you are,
                   F              Dm
The devil in disguise, hm-mm-mm.
```

Verse 1
```
F
   You fooled me with your kisses,
Dm
   You cheated and you schemed.
F                           Dm
Heaven knows how you lied to me,
           B♭      C        F
You're not the way you seemed.
```

Pre-chorus 2
```
         F
You look like an angel, walk like an angel,
B♭                               C
Talk like an angel, but I got wise.
```

Chorus 2
```
N.C.                        F
You're the devil in disguise,
                Dm
Oh yes you are,
                   F              Dm
The devil in disguise, hm-mm-mm.
```

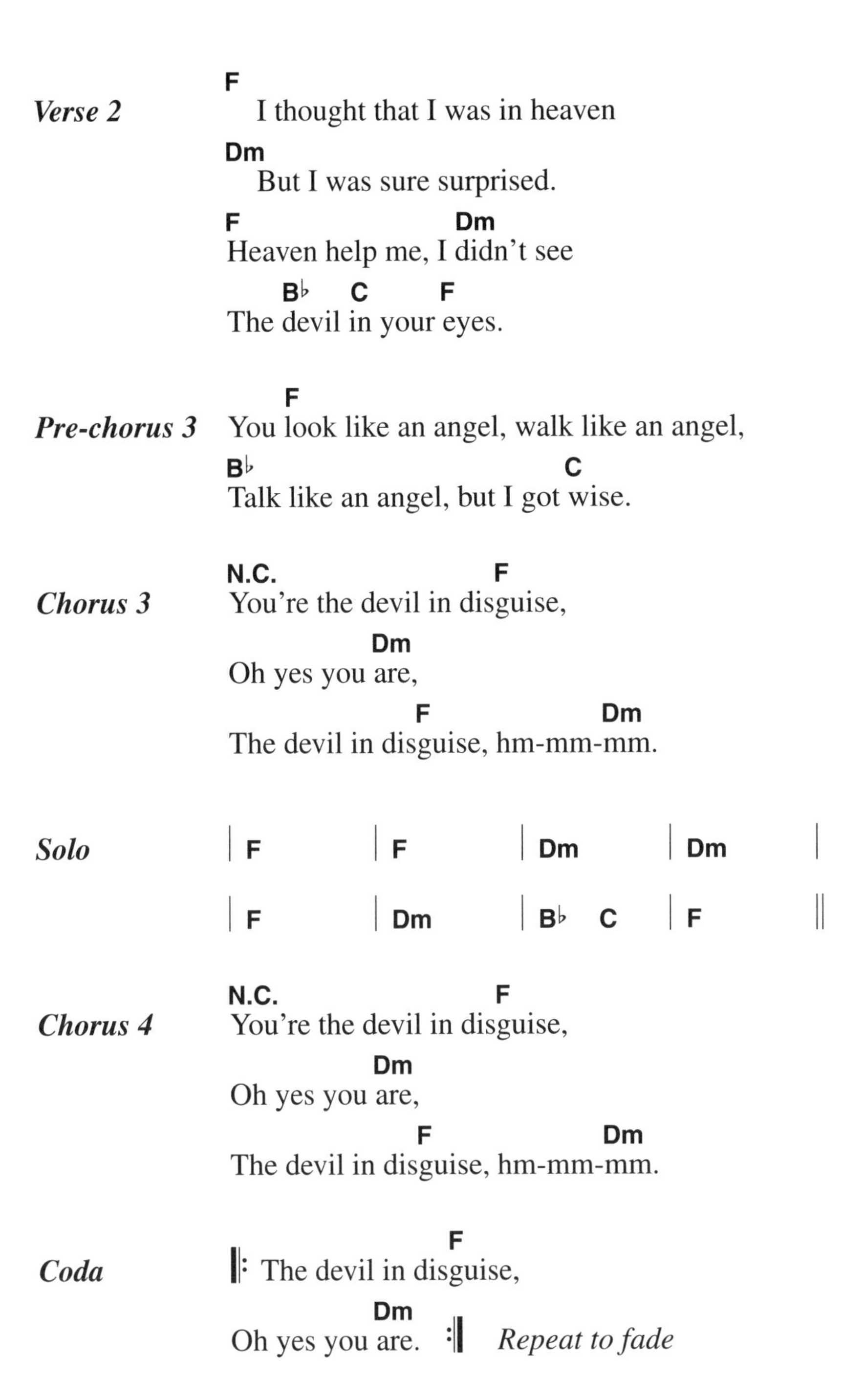

Verse 2

F
I thought that I was in heaven
Dm
But I was sure surprised.
F   Dm
Heaven help me, I didn't see
     B♭   C   F
The devil in your eyes.

Pre-chorus 3

     F
You look like an angel, walk like an angel,
B♭   C
Talk like an angel, but I got wise.

Chorus 3

N.C.   F
You're the devil in disguise,
            Dm
Oh yes you are,
               F   Dm
The devil in disguise, hm-mm-mm.

Solo

| F | F | Dm | Dm |
| F | Dm | B♭ C | F ||

Chorus 4

N.C.   F
You're the devil in disguise,
            Dm
Oh yes you are,
               F   Dm
The devil in disguise, hm-mm-mm.

Coda

                    F
𝄆 The devil in disguise,
            Dm
Oh yes you are. 𝄇 *Repeat to fade*

Viva Las Vegas

Words & Music by
Doc Pomus & Mort Shuman

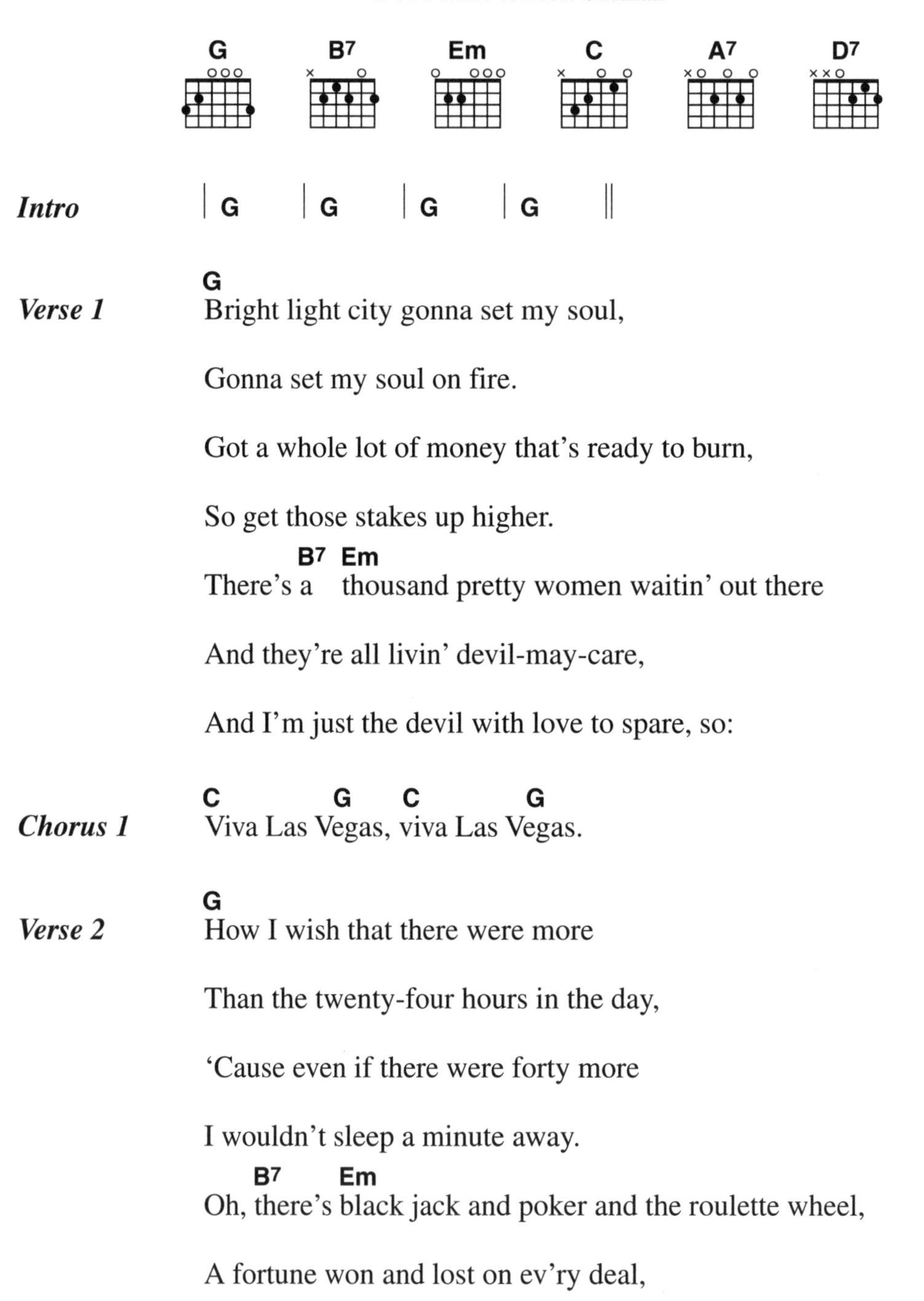

Intro | G | G | G | G ||

```
              G
Verse 1       Bright light city gonna set my soul,

              Gonna set my soul on fire.

              Got a whole lot of money that's ready to burn,

              So get those stakes up higher.
                     B7  Em
              There's a  thousand pretty women waitin' out there

              And they're all livin' devil-may-care,

              And I'm just the devil with love to spare, so:

              C           G     C          G
Chorus 1      Viva Las Vegas, viva Las Vegas.

              G
Verse 2       How I wish that there were more

              Than the twenty-four hours in the day,

              'Cause even if there were forty more

              I wouldn't sleep a minute away.
                  B7       Em
              Oh, there's black jack and poker and the roulette wheel,

              A fortune won and lost on ev'ry deal,

              All you need's a strong heart and a nerve of steel.
```

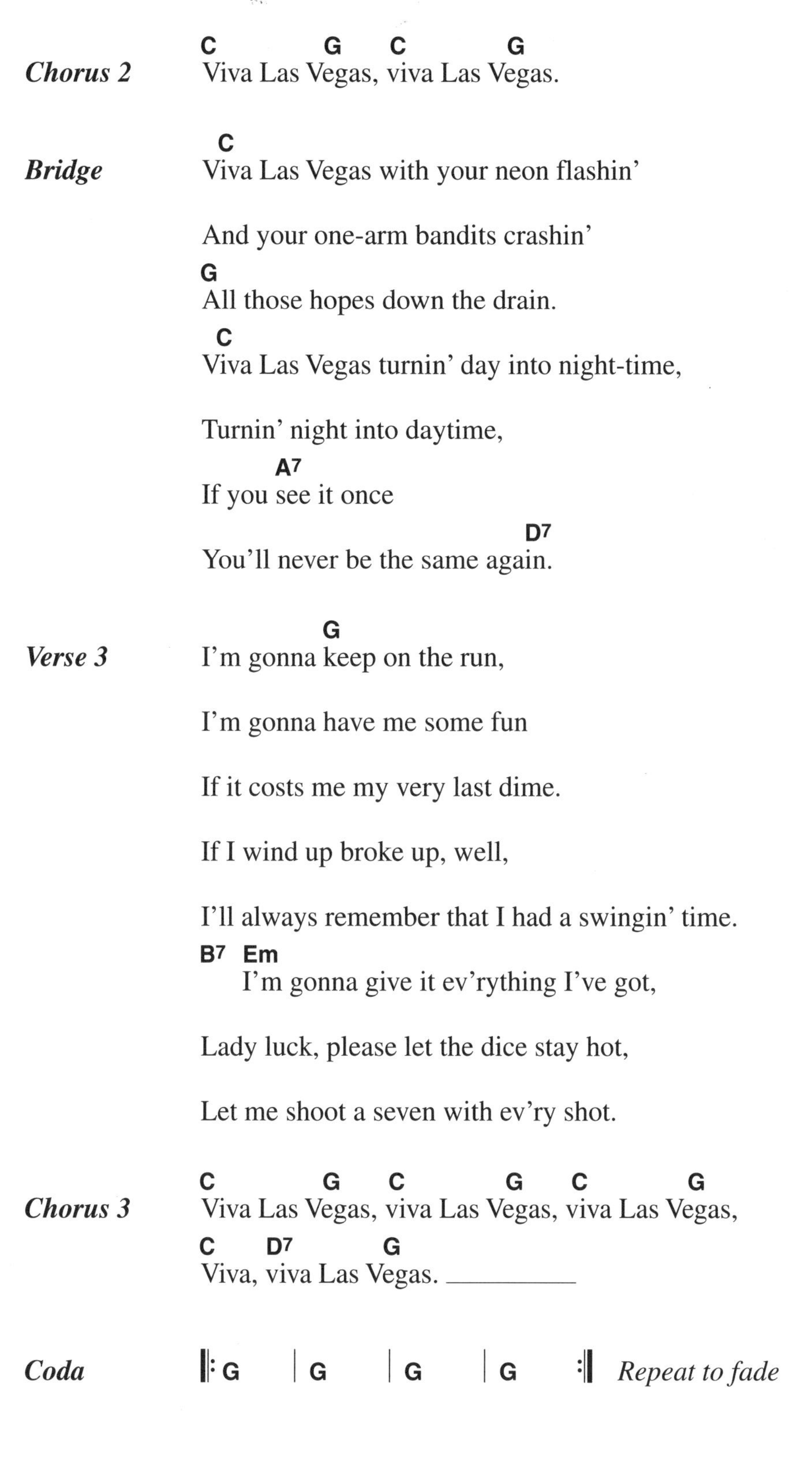

Chorus 2

C G C G
Viva Las Vegas, viva Las Vegas.

Bridge

C
Viva Las Vegas with your neon flashin'

And your one-arm bandits crashin'

G
All those hopes down the drain.

C
Viva Las Vegas turnin' day into night-time,

Turnin' night into daytime,

A7
If you see it once

D7
You'll never be the same again.

Verse 3

G
I'm gonna keep on the run,

I'm gonna have me some fun

If it costs me my very last dime.

If I wind up broke up, well,

I'll always remember that I had a swingin' time.

B7 Em
I'm gonna give it ev'rything I've got,

Lady luck, please let the dice stay hot,

Let me shoot a seven with ev'ry shot.

Chorus 3

C G C G C G
Viva Las Vegas, viva Las Vegas, viva Las Vegas,

C D7 G
Viva, viva Las Vegas. ________

Coda

|: G | G | G | G :| *Repeat to fade*

Crying In The Chapel

Words & Music by
Artie Glenn

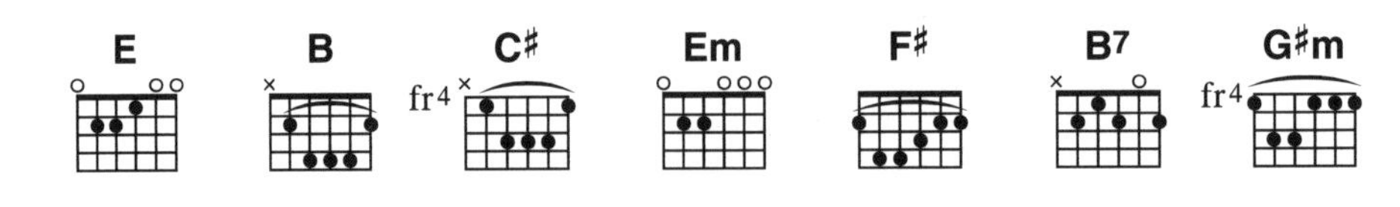

Verse 1

N.C. E
You saw me crying in the chapel,
B
The tears I shed were tears of joy,
C♯
I know the meaning of contentment
Em F♯ B E B
Now I'm happy with the Lord.

Verse 2

N.C. E
Just a plain and simple chapel
B
Where humble people go to pray.
C♯
I pray the Lord that I'll grow stronger
Em F♯ B E B B7
As I live from day to day.

Bridge 1

E Em
I've searched and I've searched
B G♯m
But I couldn't find
C♯
No way on earth
F♯
To gain peace of mind.

Verse 3

```
N.C.                   E
Now I'm happy in the chapel
                              B
Where people are of one accord.
                        C#
Yes we gather in the chapel
Em       F#                B     E  B  B7
  Just to sing and praise the Lord.
```

Bridge 2

```
       E              Em
You'll search and you'll search
    B          G#m
But you'll never find
   C#
No way on earth
               F#
To gain peace of mind.
```

Verse 4

```
N.C.                        E
Take your troubles to the chapel,
                              B
Get down on your knees and pray,
                              C#
Then your burdens will be lighter
Em          F#            B
  And you'll surely find the way

(And you'll surely find the way).
```

Love Letters

Words by Edward Heyman
Music by Victor Young

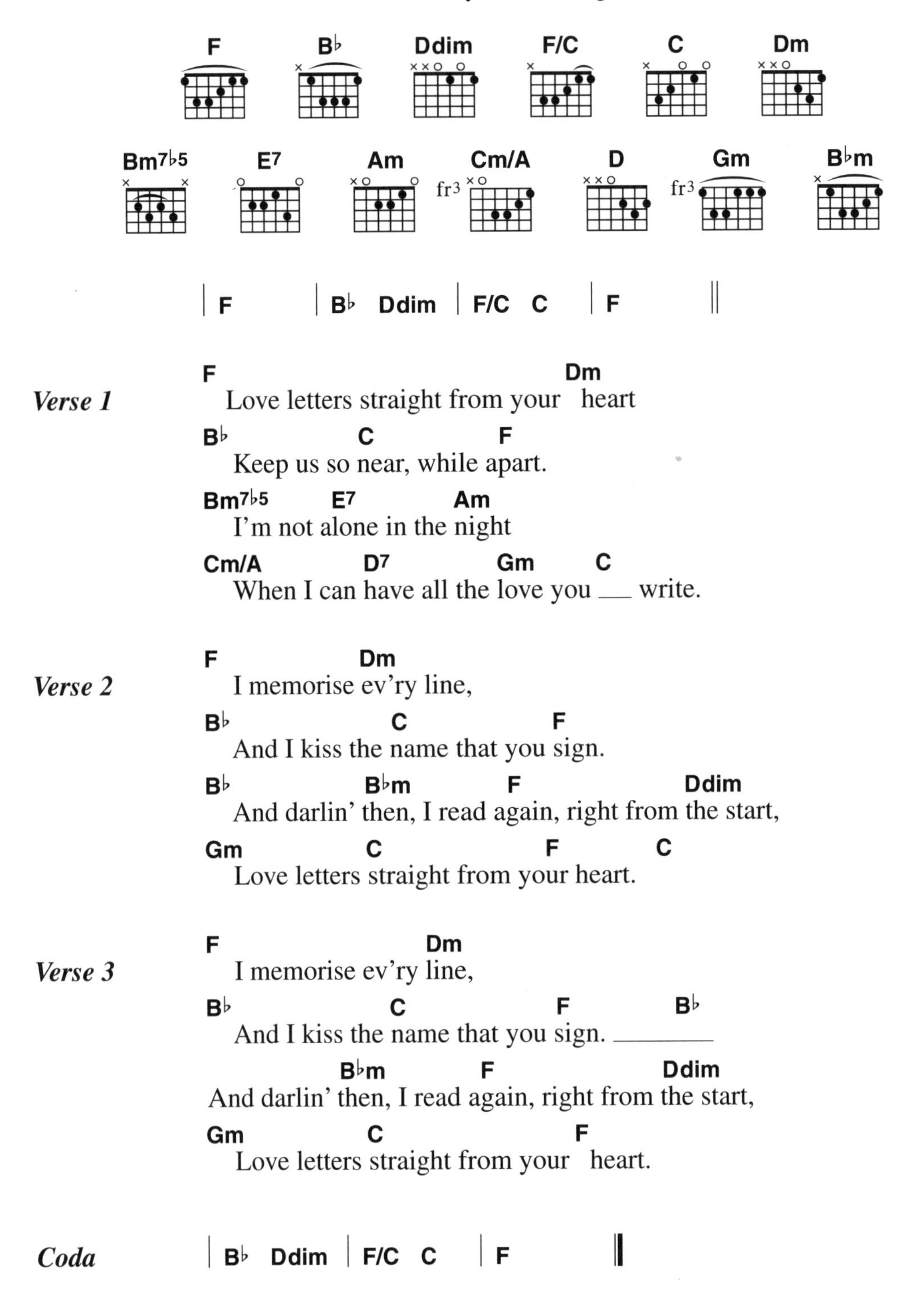

Guitar Man

Words & Music by
Jerry Hubbard

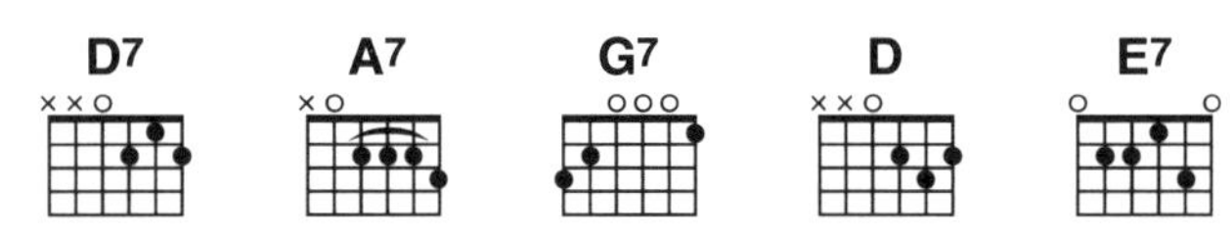

Tune guitar slightly flat

Intro | D7 | D7 | D7 A7 ||

Verse 1

```
                        D7
Well, I quit my job down at the car wash,

Left my mama a goodbye note;

By sundown I'd left Kingston,

With my guitar under my coat.
                 G7
I hitchhiked all the way down to Memphis,

Got a room at the YMCA;
          D7
For the next three weeks I went huntin' them nights,

Just lookin' for a place to play.
          A7
Well, I thought my pickin' would set 'em on fire
        G7        N.C.                 D
But nobody wanted to hire a guitar man.

| D7  A7 ||
```

Verse 2

```
                              D7
Well, I nearly 'bout starved to death down in Memphis,

I run outta money and luck,

So I bought me a ride down to Macon, Georgia,

On a overloaded poultry truck.
```

cont.

I thumbed on down to Panama City,

Started pickin' out some o' them all night bars,

D7

Hopin' I could make myself a dollar,

Makin' music on my guitar.

A7

I got the same old story at them all night piers,

G7 N.C. D7

"There ain't no room around here for a guitar man

We don't need a guitar man, son."

Bridge

G7

So I slept in the hobo jungles,

Roamed a thousand miles of track

D7

Till I found myself in Mobile Alabama,

At a club they call Big Jack's.

G7

A little four-piece band was jammin',

So I took my guitar and I sat in,

E7

I showed 'em what a band would sound like,

A7

With a swingin' little guitar man.

"Show 'em, son!"

Solo

| D7 | G7 | D7 | D |

| D7 | D7 | G7 | D7 |

| A7 G7 | D7 | D7 A7 ||

Verse 3

If you ever take a trip down to the ocean,

Find yourself down around Mobile,

Make it on out to a club called Jack's.

If you got a little time to kill

G7
Just follow that crowd of people,

You'll wind up out on his dance floor,

D7
Diggin' the finest little five-piece group,

Up and down the Gulf of Mexico.

A7
Guess who's leadin' that five-piece band?

G7 N.C. D7
Well, wouldn't ya know, it's that swingin' little guitar man.

Outro

D7	G7	D7	D
D7	D7	G7	D7
A7 G7	D7	

Fade out

If I Can Dream

Words & Music by
W. Earl Brown

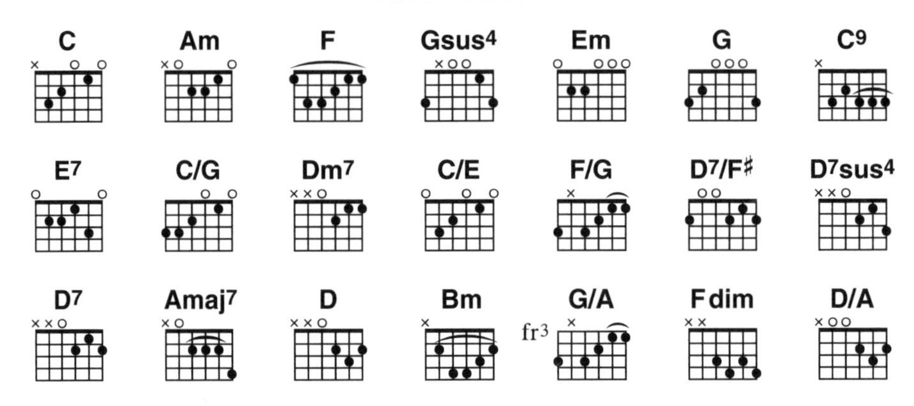

Tune guitar slightly sharp

Intro | C Am | C Am | C Am | C Am ||

Verse 1

```
                C               Am      F               Gsus4
There must be lights burning brighter somewhere,
           C     Em      Am      Em
Got to be birds   flying higher
   F       G
In a sky more blue.
```

Chorus 1

```
         C                C9
If I can dream of a better land
      F                     E7      Am
Where all my brothers walk hand in hand,
        C/G      Am
Tell me why, oh why,
   F     Dm7       C/E     Am    Dm7
Oh why can't my dream come true?
G       F/G       G
   Oh why?
```

Verse 2

```
                C                   Am       F           Gsus4
There must be peace and understanding sometime,
                  C        Em        Am          Em
Strong winds of promise   that will blow away
   F        G
The doubt and fear.
```

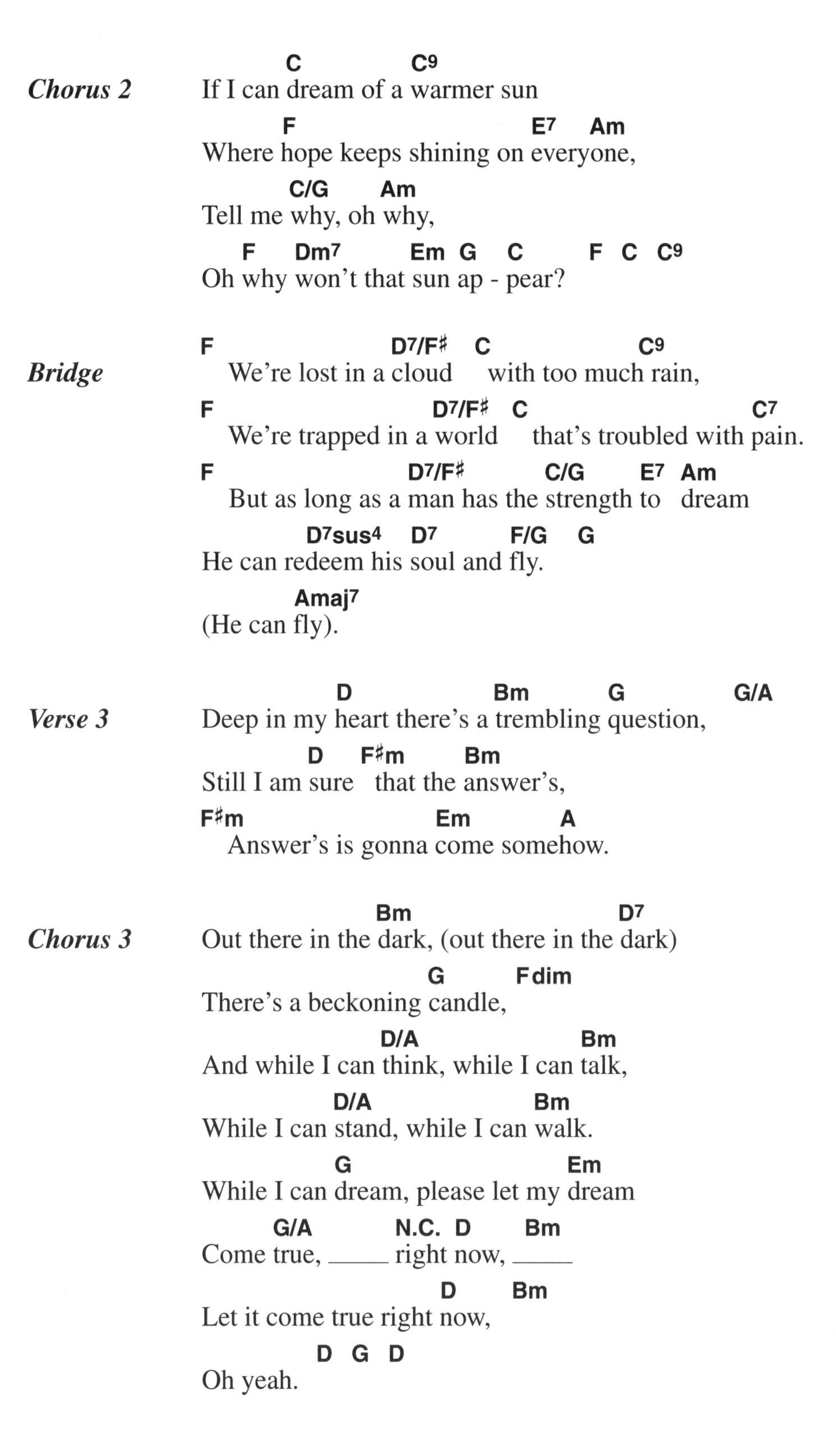

Chorus 2

C C9
If I can dream of a warmer sun
F E7 Am
Where hope keeps shining on everyone,
C/G Am
Tell me why, oh why,
F Dm7 Em G C F C C9
Oh why won't that sun ap - pear?

Bridge

F D7/F♯ C C9
We're lost in a cloud with too much rain,
F D7/F♯ C C7
We're trapped in a world that's troubled with pain.
F D7/F♯ C/G E7 Am
But as long as a man has the strength to dream
D7sus4 D7 F/G G
He can redeem his soul and fly.
Amaj7
(He can fly).

Verse 3

D Bm G G/A
Deep in my heart there's a trembling question,
D F♯m Bm
Still I am sure that the answer's,
F♯m Em A
Answer's is gonna come somehow.

Chorus 3

Bm D7
Out there in the dark, (out there in the dark)
G Fdim
There's a beckoning candle,
D/A Bm
And while I can think, while I can talk,
D/A Bm
While I can stand, while I can walk.
G Em
While I can dream, please let my dream
G/A N.C. D Bm
Come true, ____ right now, ____
D Bm
Let it come true right now,
D G D
Oh yeah.

In The Ghetto

Words & Music by
Mac Davis

A C♯m (fr4) D E C♯m7 (fr4) Bm7

Capo first fret

Intro | A ||

Verse 1

A
As the snow flies
C♯m
On a cold and grey Chicago morning
D E A
A poor little baby child is born in the ghetto,

(In the ghetto).

And his Mama cries
C♯m
'Cause if there's one thing that she don't need
D E A
It's another little hungry mouth to feed in the ghetto,

(In the ghetto).

Bridge 1

E
Ah, people don't you understand
D A
The child needs a helpin' hand,
D E A
He'll grow up to be an angry young man someday.
E
Take a look at you and me,
D A
Are we too blind to see?
D C♯m7 Bm7 E
Or do we simply turn our heads and look the other way?

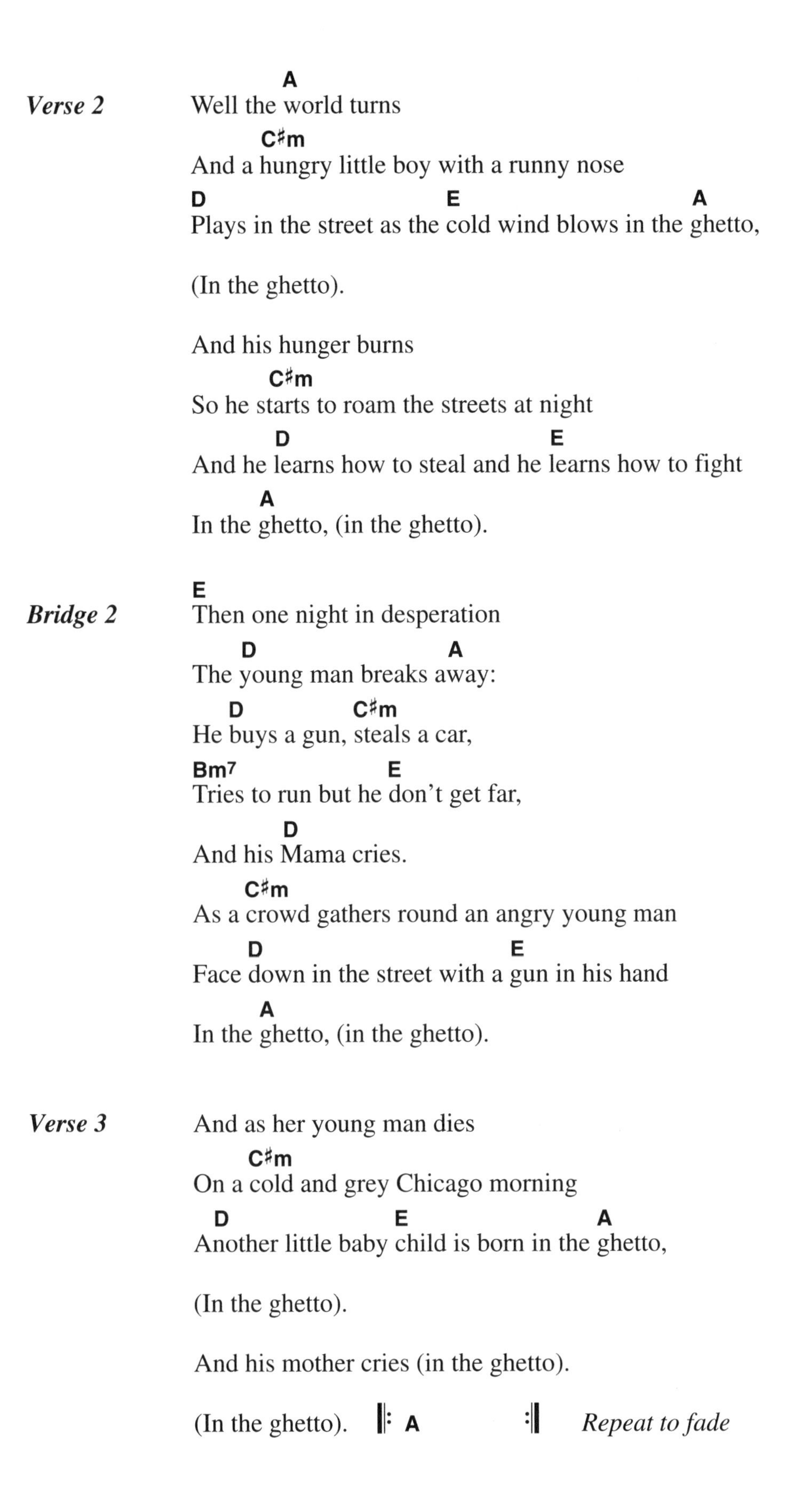

Verse 2

A
Well the world turns
C♯m
And a hungry little boy with a runny nose
D E A
Plays in the street as the cold wind blows in the ghetto,

(In the ghetto).

And his hunger burns
C♯m
So he starts to roam the streets at night
D E
And he learns how to steal and he learns how to fight
A
In the ghetto, (in the ghetto).

Bridge 2

E
Then one night in desperation
D A
The young man breaks away:
D C♯m
He buys a gun, steals a car,
Bm7 E
Tries to run but he don't get far,
D
And his Mama cries.
C♯m
As a crowd gathers round an angry young man
D E
Face down in the street with a gun in his hand
A
In the ghetto, (in the ghetto).

Verse 3

And as her young man dies
C♯m
On a cold and grey Chicago morning
D E A
Another little baby child is born in the ghetto,

(In the ghetto).

And his mother cries (in the ghetto).

(In the ghetto). 𝄆 A 𝄇 *Repeat to fade*

Suspicious Minds

Words & Music by
Francis Zambon

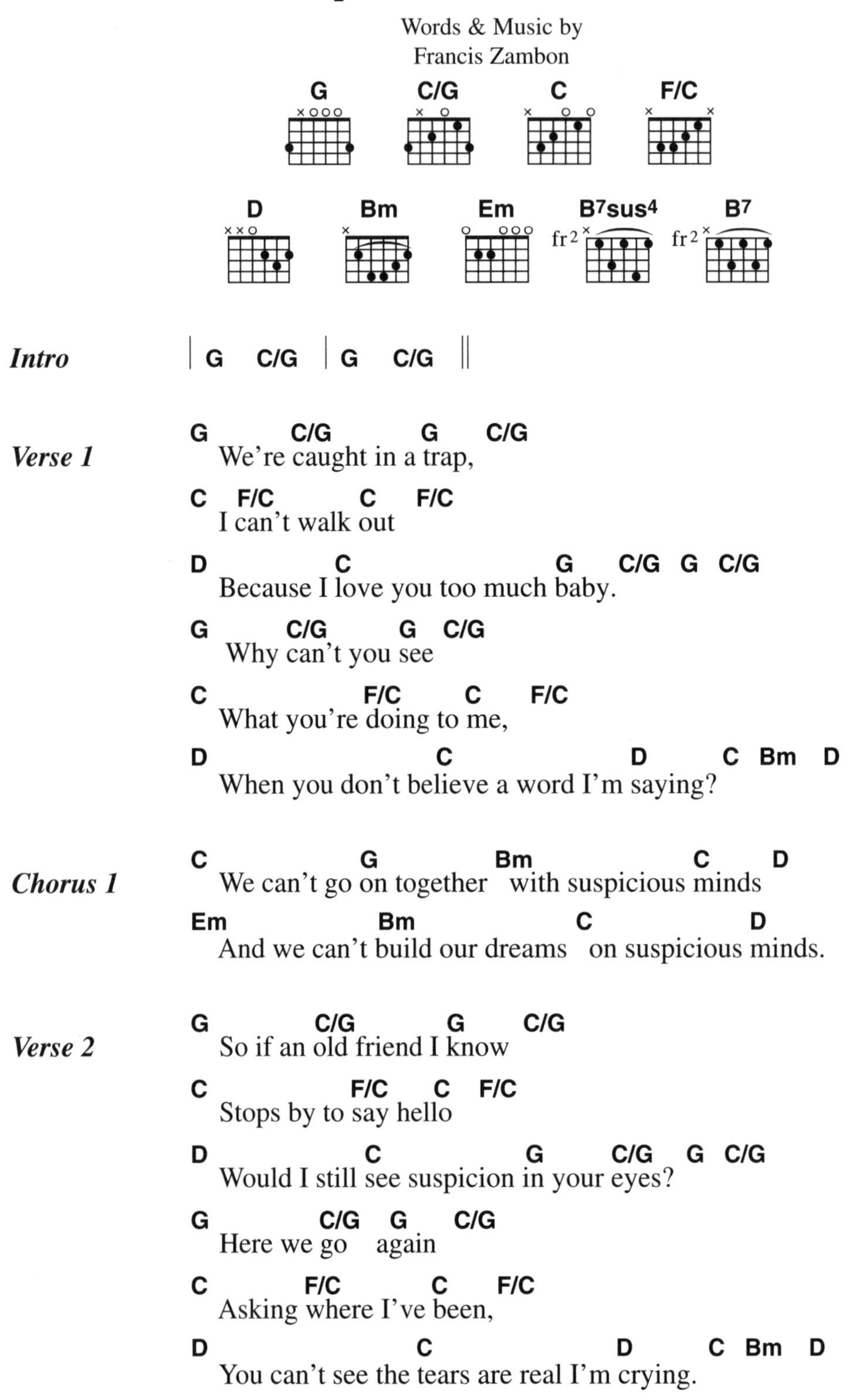

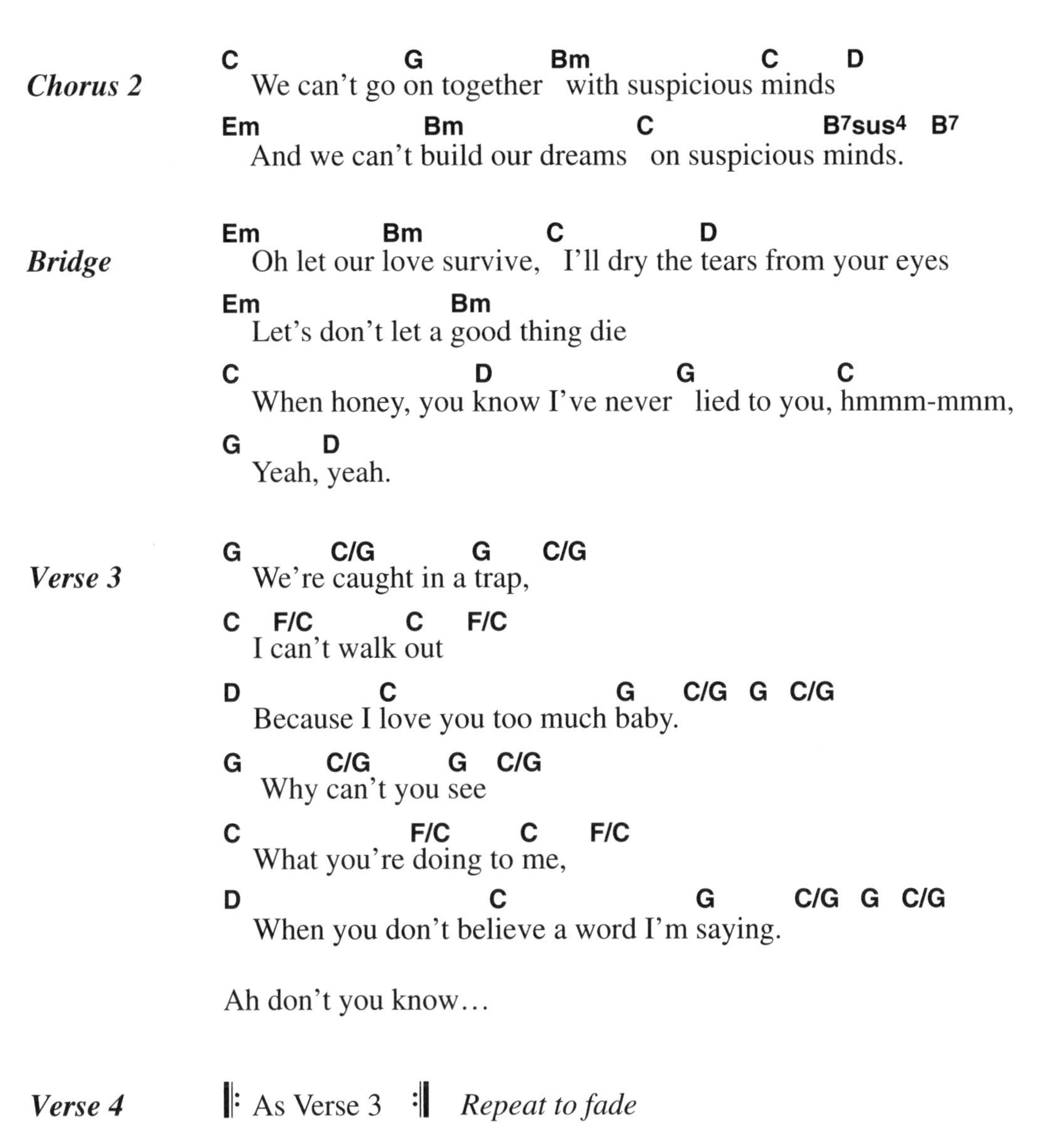

Chorus 2

C G Bm C D
We can't go on together with suspicious minds

Em Bm C B^{7}sus^{4} B^{7}
And we can't build our dreams on suspicious minds.

Bridge

Em Bm C D
Oh let our love survive, I'll dry the tears from your eyes

Em Bm
Let's don't let a good thing die

C D G C
When honey, you know I've never lied to you, hmmm-mmm,

G D
Yeah, yeah.

Verse 3

G C/G G C/G
We're caught in a trap,

C F/C C F/C
I can't walk out

D C G C/G G C/G
Because I love you too much baby.

G C/G G C/G
Why can't you see

C F/C C F/C
What you're doing to me,

D C G C/G G C/G
When you don't believe a word I'm saying.

Ah don't you know…

Verse 4

𝄆 As Verse 3 𝄇 *Repeat to fade*

Don't Cry Daddy

Words & Music by
Mac Davis

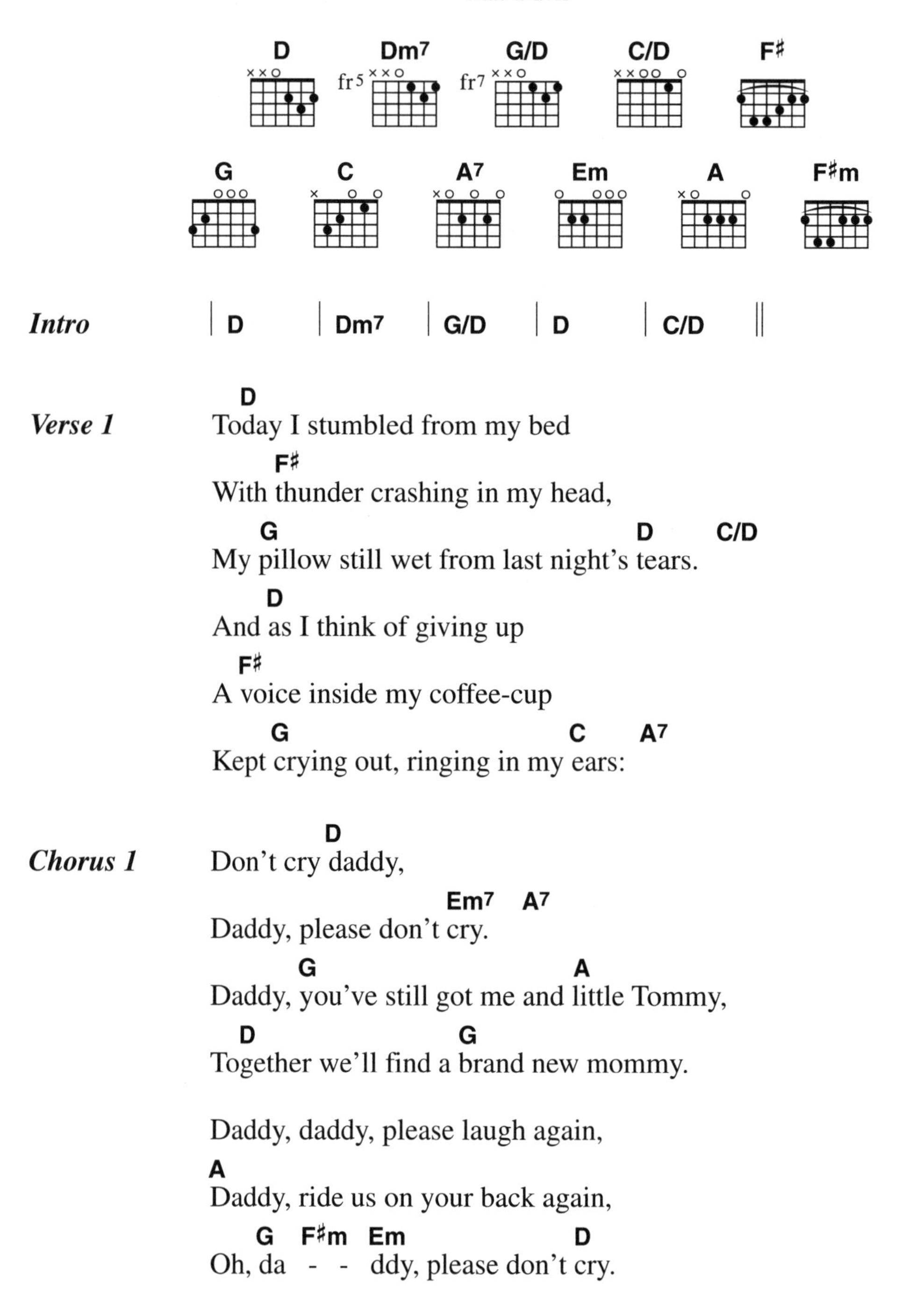

Intro | D | Dm7 | G/D | D | C/D ||

Verse 1

D
Today I stumbled from my bed
F♯
With thunder crashing in my head,
G D C/D
My pillow still wet from last night's tears.
D
And as I think of giving up
F♯
A voice inside my coffee-cup
G C A7
Kept crying out, ringing in my ears:

Chorus 1

D
Don't cry daddy,
Em7 A7
Daddy, please don't cry.
G A
Daddy, you've still got me and little Tommy,
D G
Together we'll find a brand new mommy.

Daddy, daddy, please laugh again,
A
Daddy, ride us on your back again,
G F♯m Em D
Oh, da - - ddy, please don't cry.

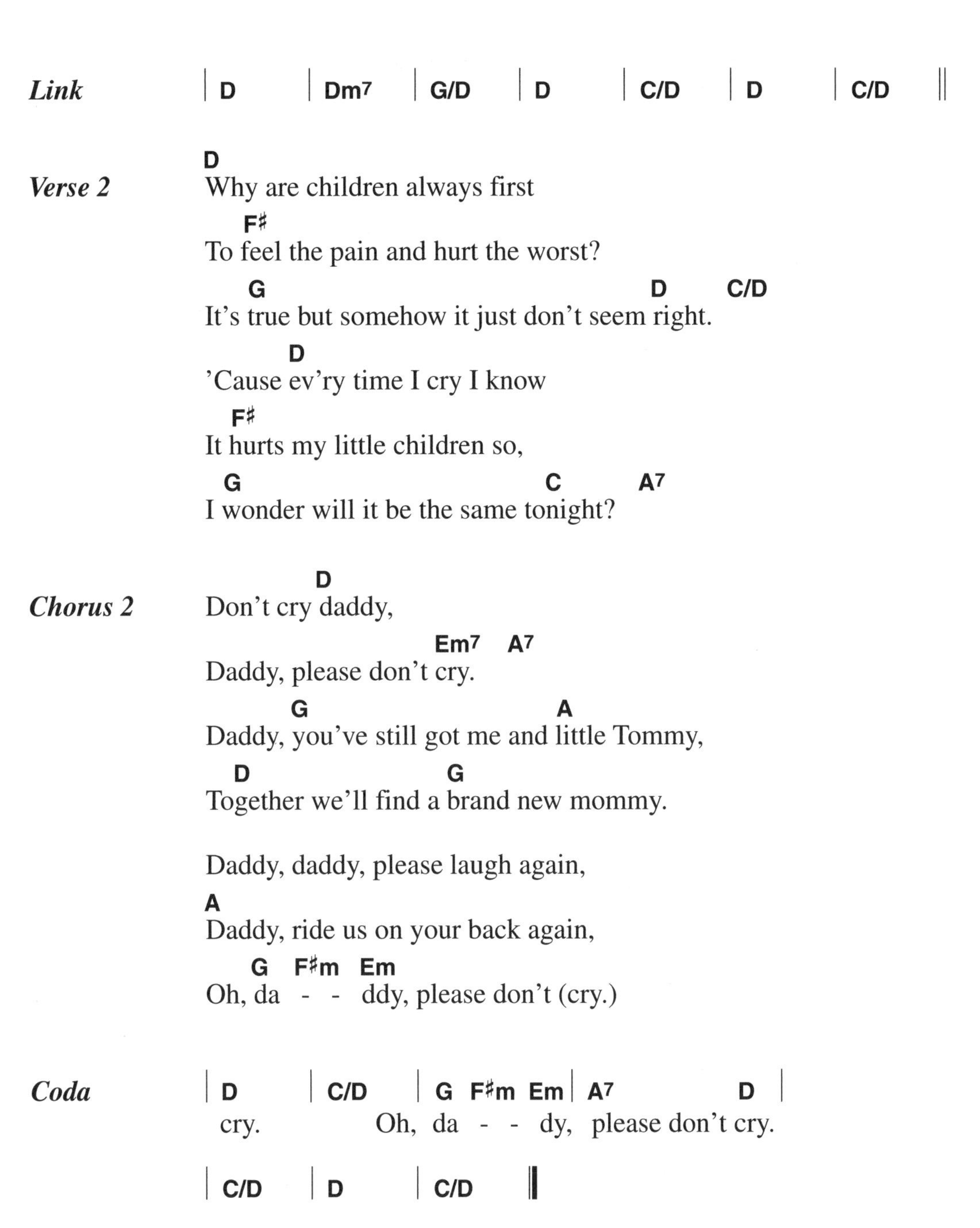

Link | D | Dm7 | G/D | D | C/D | D | C/D ||

Verse 2

D
Why are children always first
F♯
To feel the pain and hurt the worst?
G D C/D
It's true but somehow it just don't seem right.
D
'Cause ev'ry time I cry I know
F♯
It hurts my little children so,
G C A7
I wonder will it be the same tonight?

Chorus 2

D
Don't cry daddy,
Em7 A7
Daddy, please don't cry.
G A
Daddy, you've still got me and little Tommy,
D G
Together we'll find a brand new mommy.

Daddy, daddy, please laugh again,
A
Daddy, ride us on your back again,
G F♯m Em
Oh, da - - ddy, please don't (cry.)

Coda | D | C/D | G F♯m Em | A7 D |
cry. Oh, da - - dy, please don't cry.

| C/D | D | C/D ||

The Wonder Of You

Words & Music by
Baker Knight

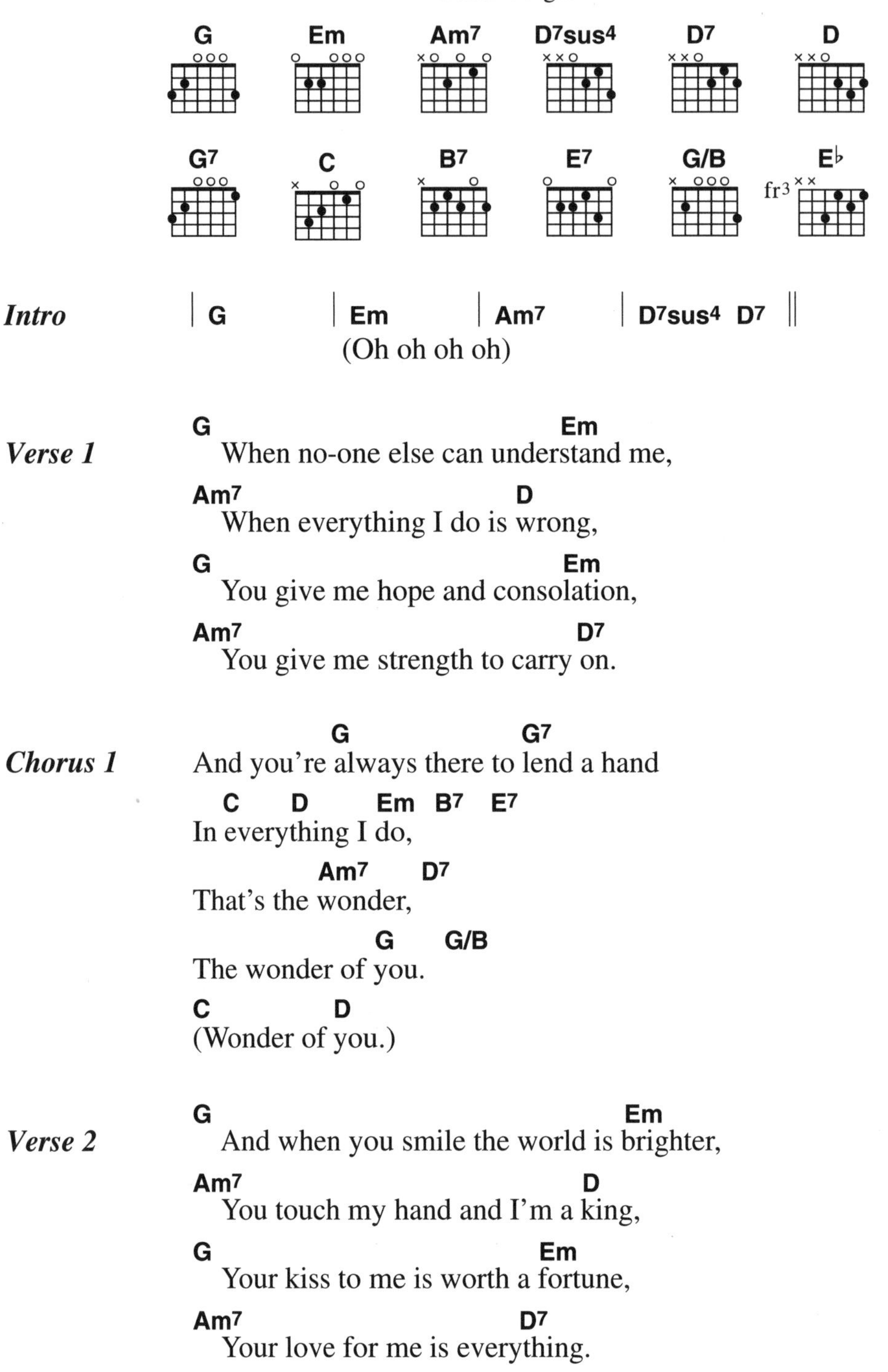

Intro | G | Em | Am7 | D7sus4 D7 ||
(Oh oh oh oh)

Verse 1

```
G                                   Em
   When no-one else can understand me,
Am7                            D
   When everything I do is wrong,
G                                   Em
   You give me hope and consolation,
Am7                                  D7
   You give me strength to carry on.
```

Chorus 1

```
               G                G7
And you're always there to lend a hand
   C      D        Em  B7   E7
In everything I do,
             Am7      D7
That's the wonder,
                 G      G/B
The wonder of you.
C            D
(Wonder of you.)
```

Verse 2

```
G                                       Em
   And when you smile the world is brighter,
Am7                                  D
   You touch my hand and I'm a king,
G                                 Em
   Your kiss to me is worth a fortune,
Am7                            D7
   Your love for me is everything.
```

Chorus 2
G G7
I guess I'll never know the reason why
C D Em B7 E7
You love me as you do.
Am7 D7
That's the wonder,
G Em C D
The wonder of you.
Solo
| G | Em | Am7 | D |
(Oh oh oh oh) (Oh oh oh
| G | Em | Am7 | D7 ||
oh) (Oh oh oh oh)
Chorus 3
G G7
I guess I'll never know the reason why
C D Em B7 E7
You love me as you do.
Am7 D7
That's the wonder,
G C E♭ G
The wonder of you.

An American Trilogy

Traditional, arranged by Mickey Newbury

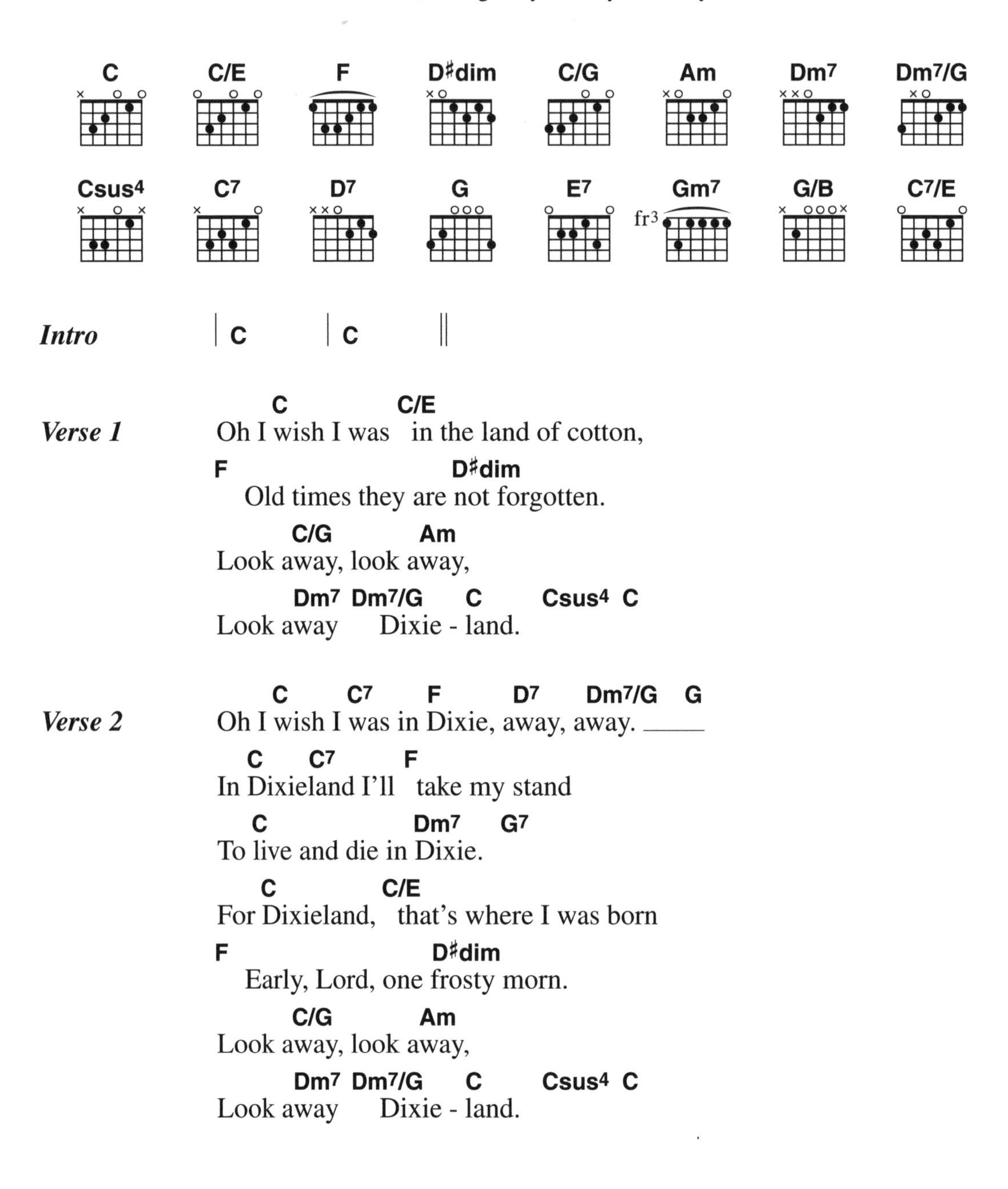

Intro | C | C ||

Verse 1

```
         C          C/E
Oh I wish I was   in the land of cotton,
F                        D♯dim
   Old times they are not forgotten.
       C/G         Am
Look away, look away,
       Dm7 Dm7/G      C       Csus4 C
Look away      Dixie - land.
```

Verse 2

```
         C      C7     F        D7     Dm7/G   G
Oh I wish I was in Dixie, away, away. ____
   C     C7       F
In Dixieland I'll   take my stand
   C               Dm7     G7
To live and die in Dixie.
     C          C/E
For Dixieland,   that's where I was born
F                      D♯dim
   Early, Lord, one frosty morn.
       C/G         Am
Look away, look away,
       Dm7 Dm7/G      C       Csus4 C
Look away      Dixie - land.
```

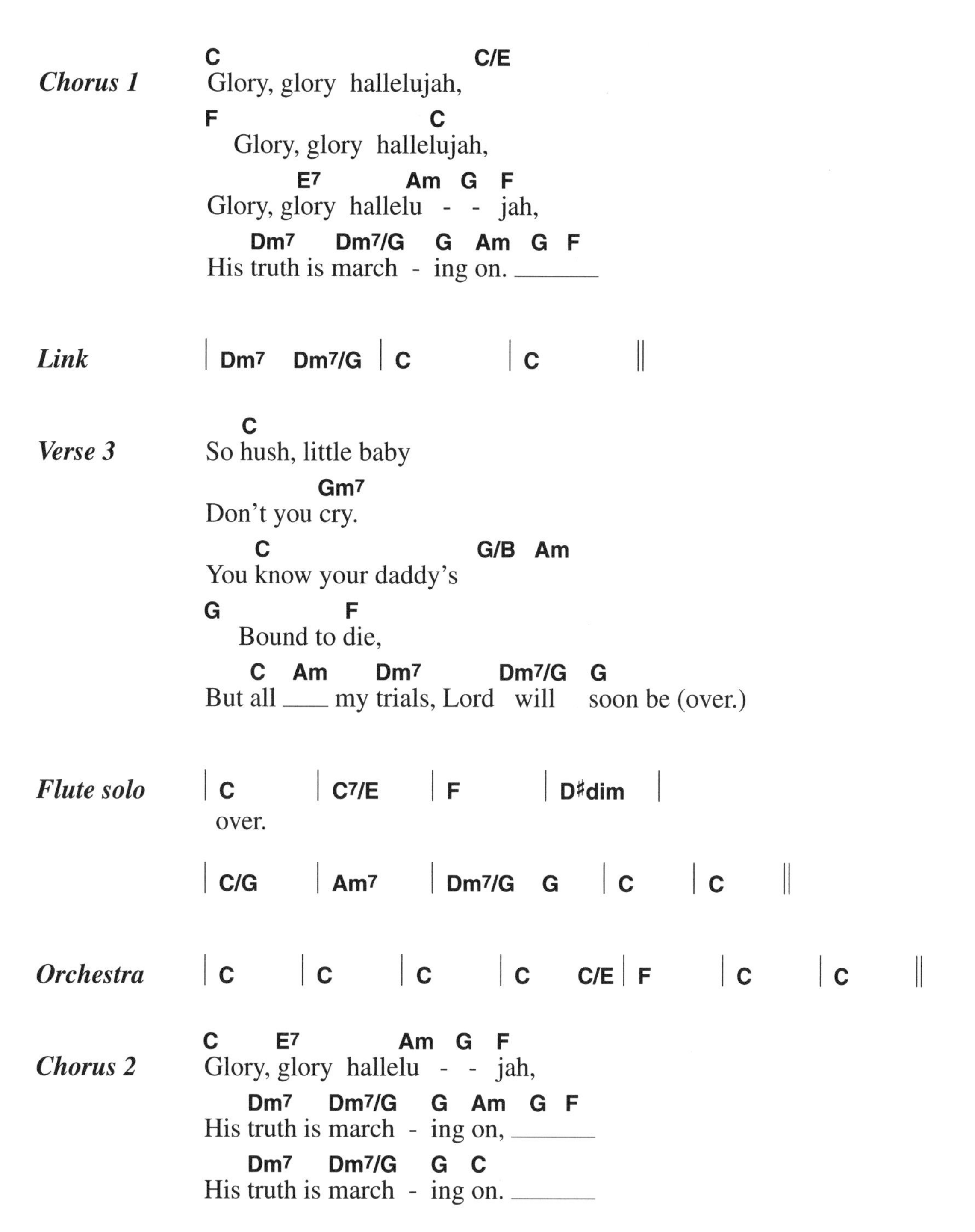
Chorus 1
C C/E
Glory, glory hallelujah,
F C
Glory, glory hallelujah,
E7 Am G F
Glory, glory hallelu - - jah,
Dm7 Dm7/G G Am G F
His truth is march - ing on.
Link
| Dm7 Dm7/G | C | C ||
Verse 3
C
So hush, little baby
Gm7
Don't you cry.
C G/B Am
You know your daddy's
G F
Bound to die,
C Am Dm7 Dm7/G G
But all my trials, Lord will soon be (over.)
Flute solo
| C | C7/E | F | D♯dim |
over.
| C/G | Am7 | Dm7/G G | C | C ||
Orchestra
| C | C | C | C C/E | F | C | C ||
Chorus 2
C E7 Am G F
Glory, glory hallelu - - jah,
Dm7 Dm7/G G Am G F
His truth is march - ing on,
Dm7 Dm7/G G C
His truth is march - ing on.

Burning Love

Words & Music by
Dennis Linde

D Dsus4 G A Bm

Intro | D Dsus4 D | D Dsus4 D | D Dsus4 D | D Dsus4 D ||

Verse 1
D G A D
Lord Almighty, I feel my temperature rising
G A D
Higher and higher, it's burning through my soul.
G A D
Girl, girl, girl, girl, you're gonna set me on fire,
G A D
My brain is flaming, I don't know which way to go, yeah.

Chorus 1
Bm A G
Your kisses lift me higher,
Bm A G
Like the sweet song of a choir.
Bm A G
You light my morning sky
A D Dsus4 D | D Dsus4 D ||
With burning love.

Verse 2
D G A D
Ooh ooh ooh ooh, I feel my temperature rising,
G A D
Help me I'm flaming, I must be one hundred and nine.
G A D
Burning, burning, burning and nothing can cool me, yeah,
G A D
I just might turn to smoke but I feel fine.

Chorus 2 As Chorus 1

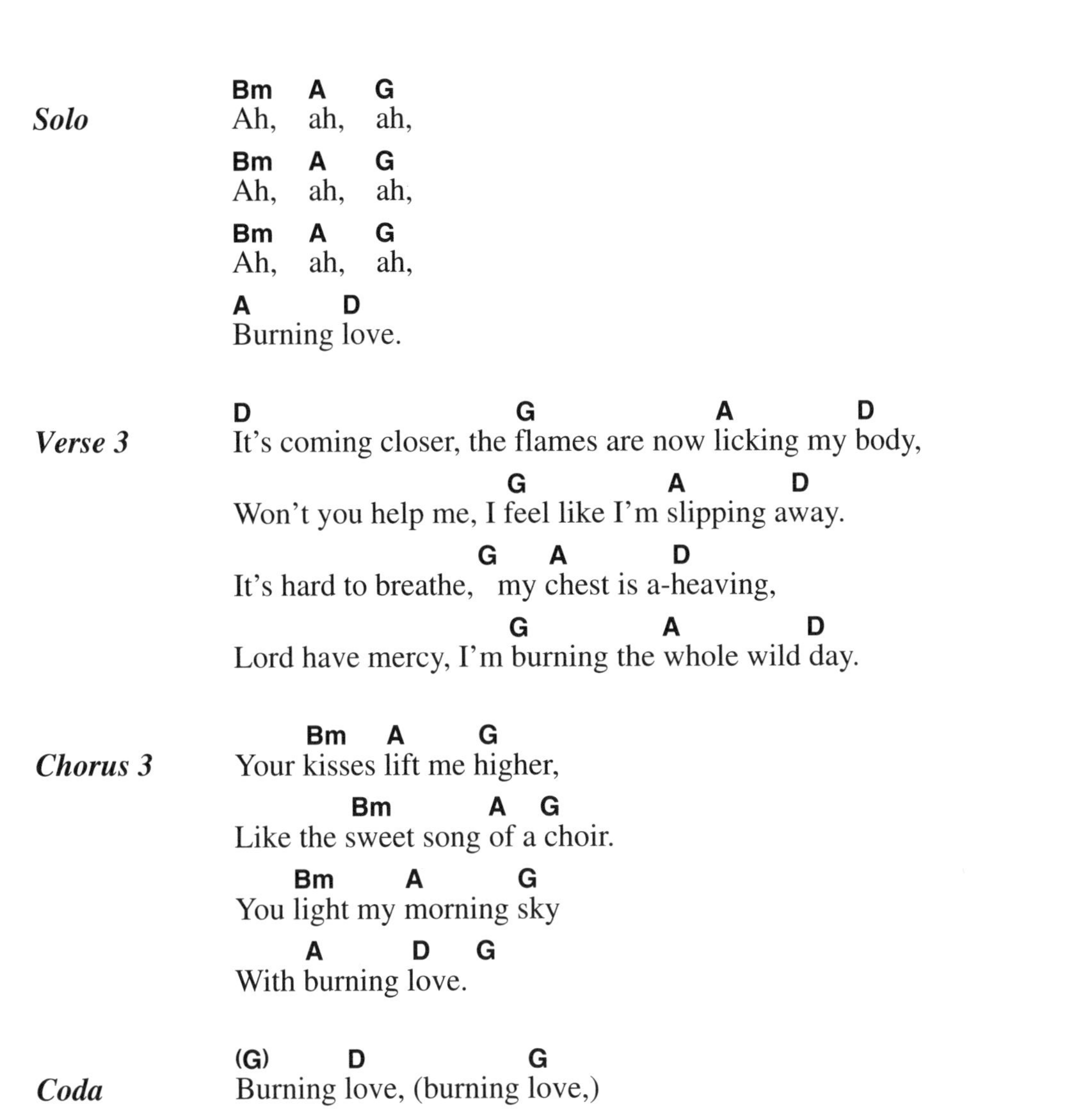

Solo

Bm A G
Ah, ah, ah,

Bm A G
Ah, ah, ah,

Bm A G
Ah, ah, ah,

A D
Burning love.

Verse 3

D G A D
It's coming closer, the flames are now licking my body,

G A D
Won't you help me, I feel like I'm slipping away.

G A D
It's hard to breathe, my chest is a-heaving,

G A D
Lord have mercy, I'm burning the whole wild day.

Chorus 3

Bm A G
Your kisses lift me higher,

Bm A G
Like the sweet song of a choir.

Bm A G
You light my morning sky

A D G
With burning love.

Coda

(G) D G
Burning love, (burning love,)

D G
𝄆 I'm just a hunk-a-hunk of burning love. 𝄇 *Repeat to fade*

Always On My Mind

Words & Music by
Wayne Thompson, Mark James & Johnny Christopher

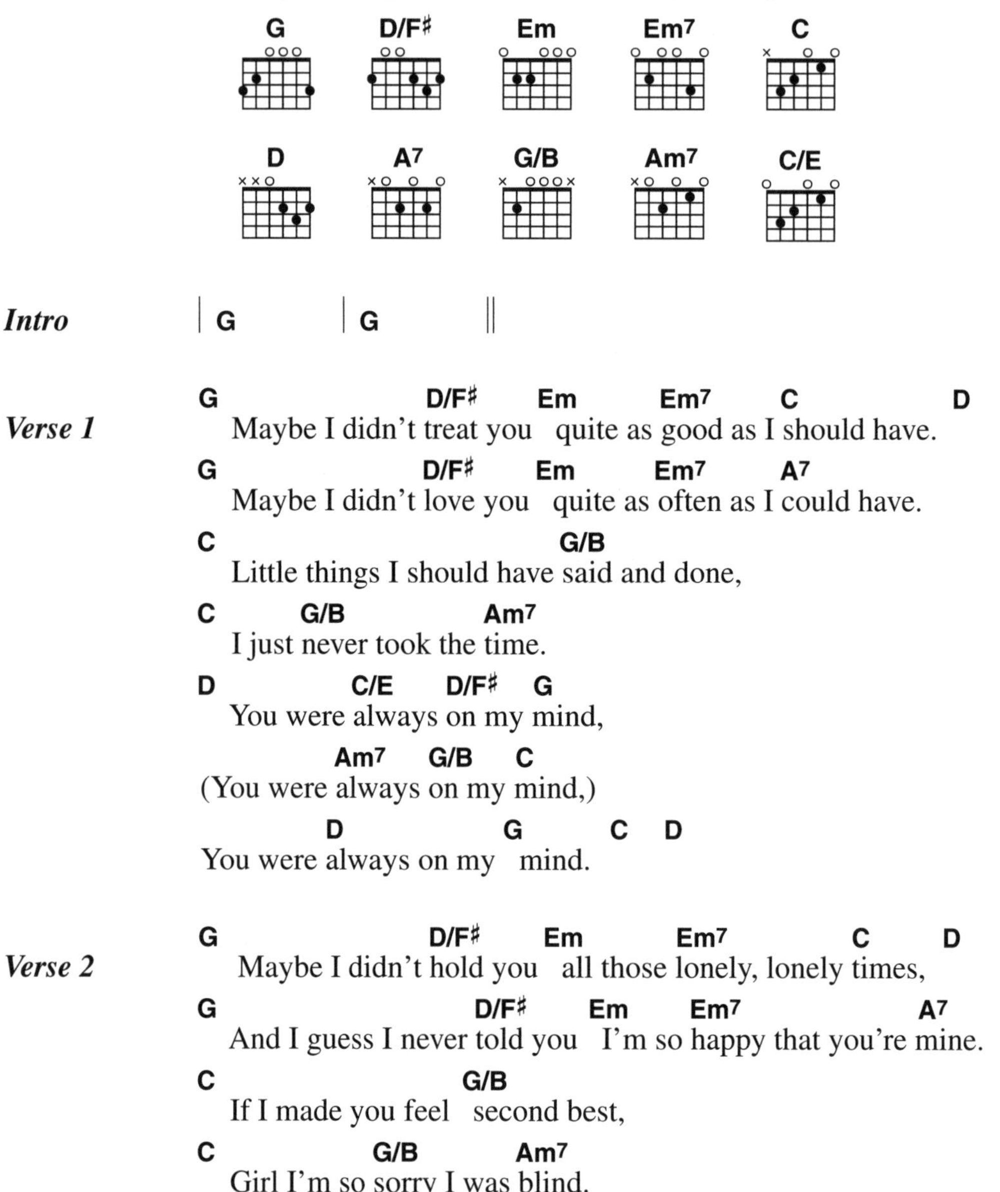

Intro | G | G ||

Verse 1

G D/F♯ Em Em7 C D
Maybe I didn't treat you quite as good as I should have.
G D/F♯ Em Em7 A7
Maybe I didn't love you quite as often as I could have.
C G/B
Little things I should have said and done,
C G/B Am7
I just never took the time.
D C/E D/F♯ G
You were always on my mind,
Am7 G/B C
(You were always on my mind,)
D G C D
You were always on my mind.

Verse 2

G D/F♯ Em Em7 C D
Maybe I didn't hold you all those lonely, lonely times,
G D/F♯ Em Em7 A7
And I guess I never told you I'm so happy that you're mine.
C G/B
If I made you feel second best,
C G/B Am7
Girl I'm so sorry I was blind.
D C/E D/F♯ G
You were always on my mind,
Am7 G/B C
(You were always on my mind,)
D G C D
You were always on my mind.

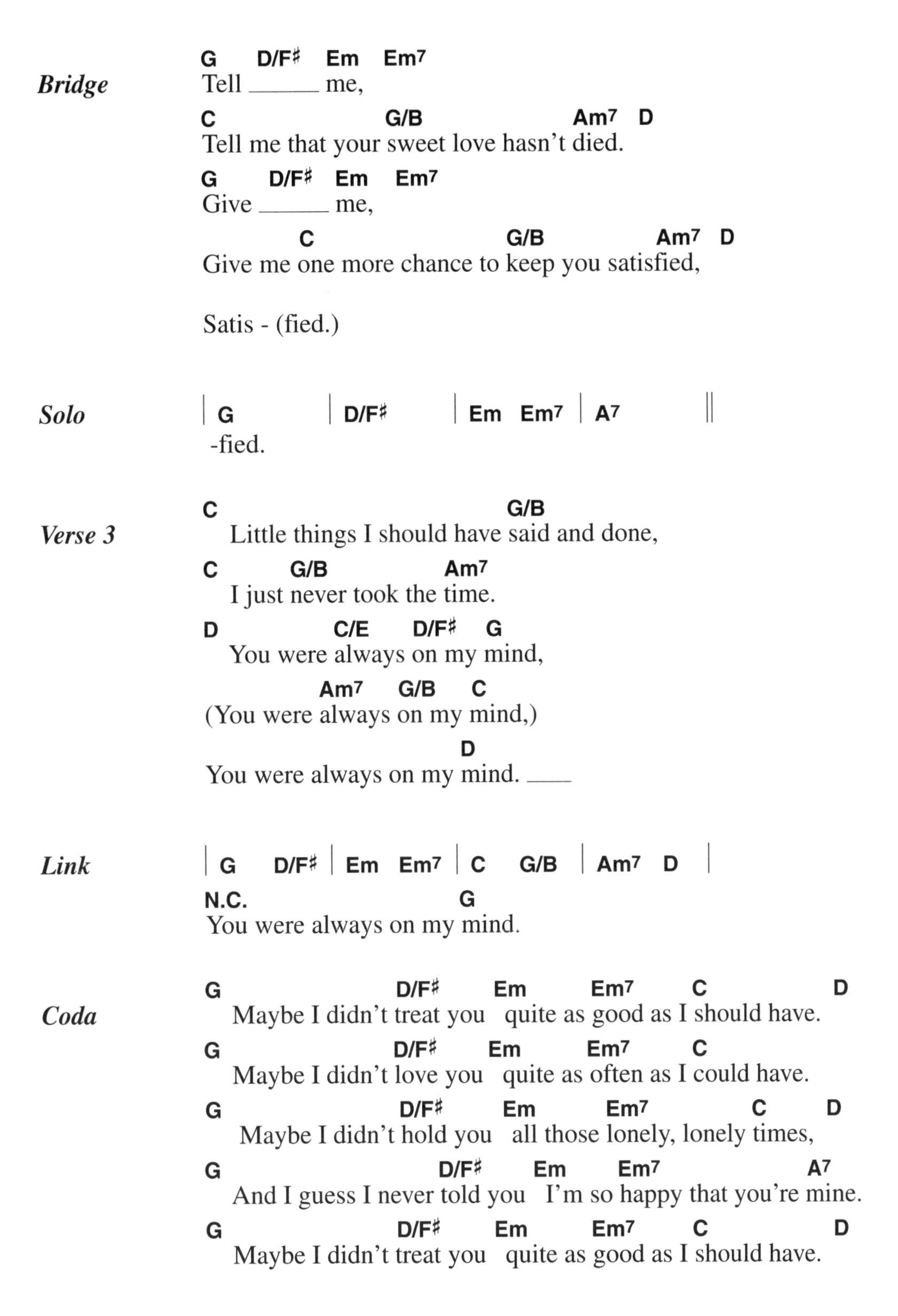

Bridge

G D/F♯ Em Em7
Tell ______ me,

C G/B Am7 D
Tell me that your sweet love hasn't died.

G D/F♯ Em Em7
Give ______ me,

C G/B Am7 D
Give me one more chance to keep you satisfied,

Satis - (fied.)

Solo

| G | D/F♯ | Em Em7 | A7 ||
-fied.

Verse 3

C G/B
Little things I should have said and done,

C G/B Am7
I just never took the time.

D C/E D/F♯ G
You were always on my mind,

Am7 G/B C
(You were always on my mind,)

D
You were always on my mind. ____

Link

| G D/F♯ | Em Em7 | C G/B | Am7 D |

N.C. G
You were always on my mind.

Coda

G D/F♯ Em Em7 C D
Maybe I didn't treat you quite as good as I should have.

G D/F♯ Em Em7 C
Maybe I didn't love you quite as often as I could have.

G D/F♯ Em Em7 C D
Maybe I didn't hold you all those lonely, lonely times,

G D/F♯ Em Em7 A7
And I guess I never told you I'm so happy that you're mine.

G D/F♯ Em Em7 C D
Maybe I didn't treat you quite as good as I should have.

Suspicion

Words & Music by
Doc Pomus & Mort Shuman

D Em7 Bm D/A A7

Tune guitar slighty sharp

Intro |: D | D | Em7 | Em7 :|

Verse 1
```
D
Ev'rytime you kiss me
                               Em7
I'm still not certain that you love me.

Ev'ry time you hold me
                               D
I'm still not certain that you care.

Though you keep on saying
                             Em7
You really, really, really love me,

Do you speak the same words
                                  D
To someone else when I'm not there?
```

Chorus 1
```
     Bm                    D/A
Suspicion torments my heart,
     Bm                D/A
Suspicion keeps us apart;
     Bm              A7
Suspicion, why torture me?
```

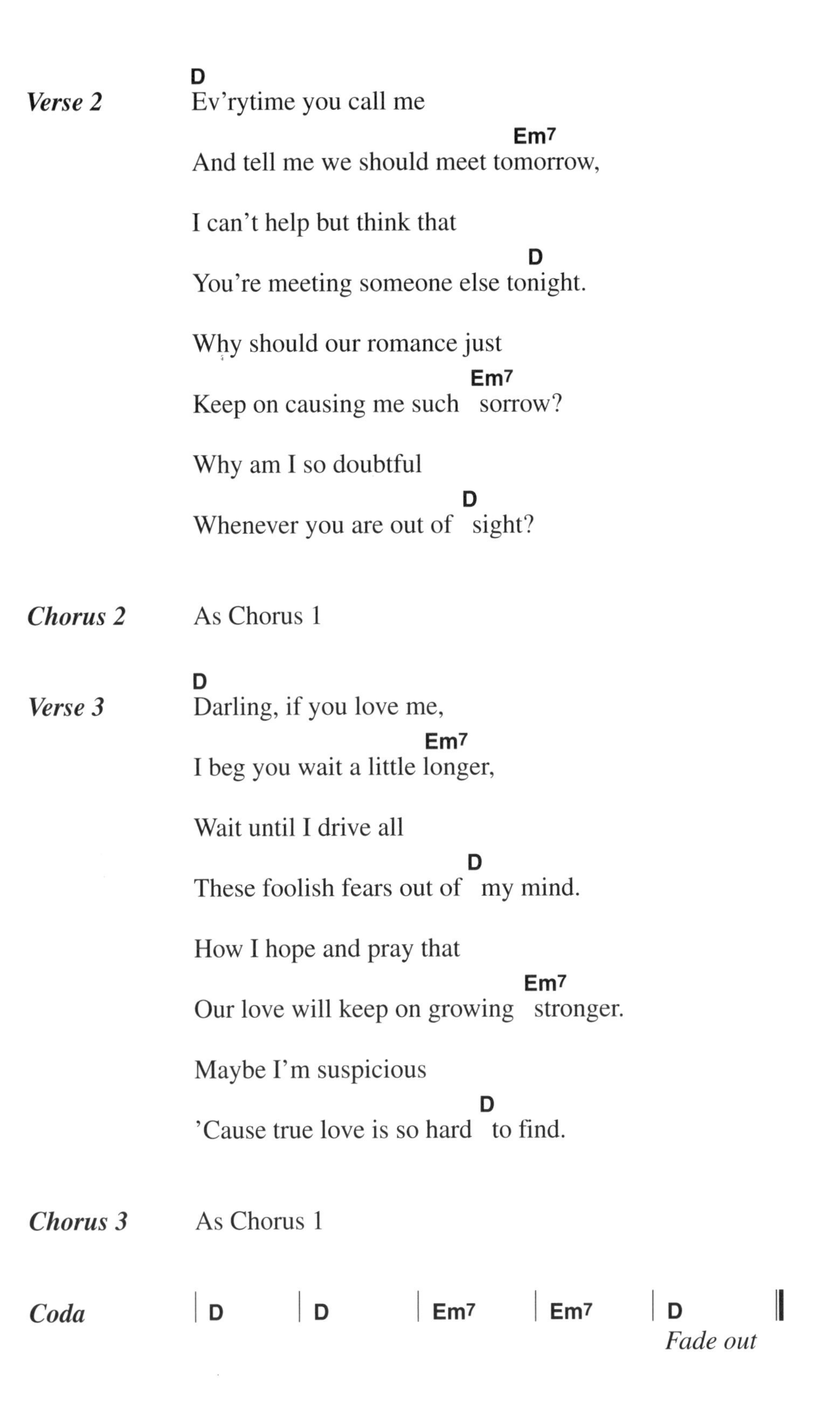

Verse 2

D
Ev'rytime you call me

Em7
And tell me we should meet tomorrow,

I can't help but think that

D
You're meeting someone else tonight.

Why should our romance just

Em7
Keep on causing me such sorrow?

Why am I so doubtful

D
Whenever you are out of sight?

Chorus 2 As Chorus 1

Verse 3

D
Darling, if you love me,

Em7
I beg you wait a little longer,

Wait until I drive all

D
These foolish fears out of my mind.

How I hope and pray that

Em7
Our love will keep on growing stronger.

Maybe I'm suspicious

D
'Cause true love is so hard to find.

Chorus 3 As Chorus 1

Coda | D | D | Em7 | Em7 | D ‖
Fade out

Moody Blue

Words & Music by
Mark James

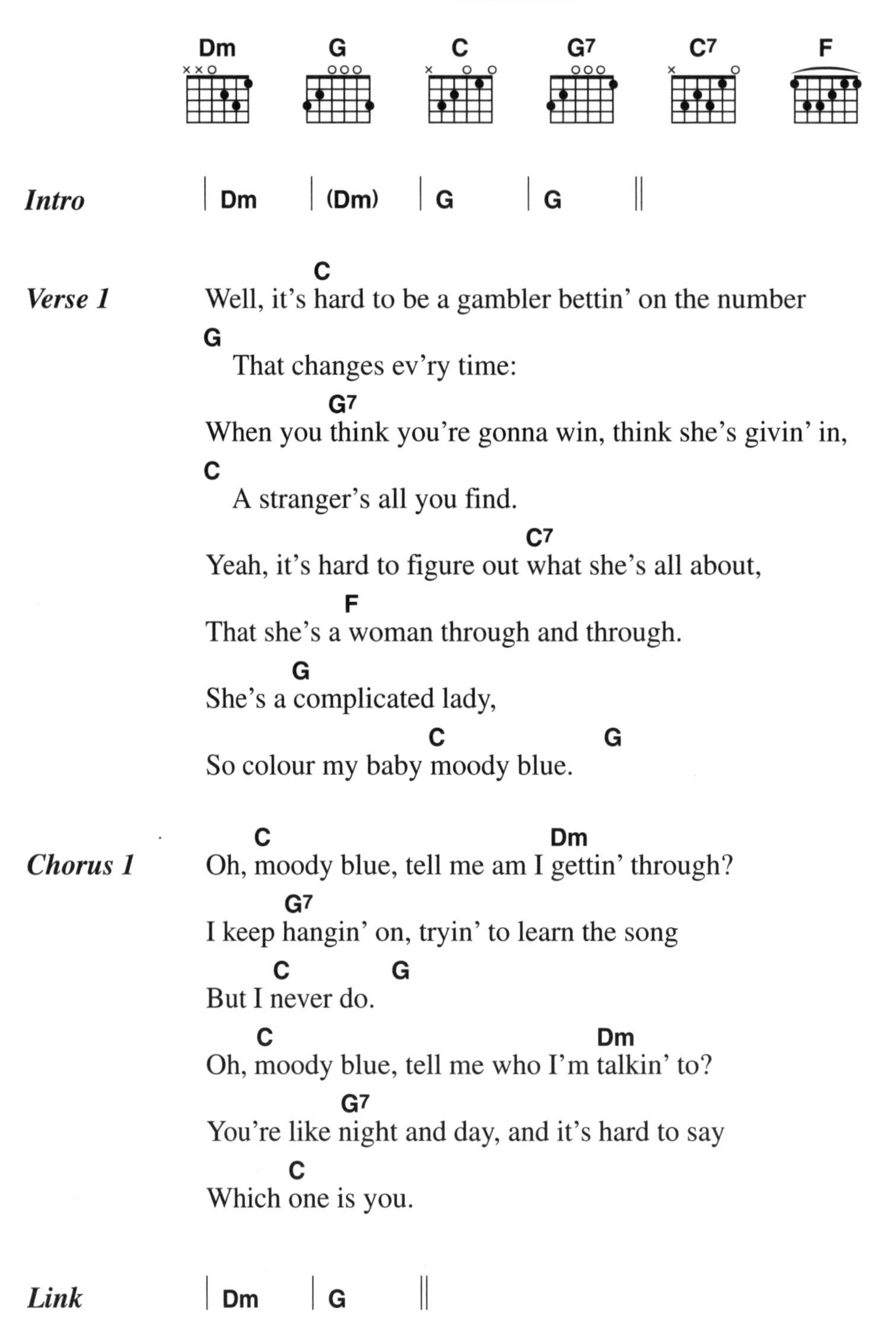

Dm G C G7 C7 F

Intro | Dm | (Dm) | G | G ||

Verse 1

C
Well, it's hard to be a gambler bettin' on the number
G
That changes ev'ry time:
G7
When you think you're gonna win, think she's givin' in,
C
A stranger's all you find.
C7
Yeah, it's hard to figure out what she's all about,
F
That she's a woman through and through.
G
She's a complicated lady,
C G
So colour my baby moody blue.

Chorus 1

C Dm
Oh, moody blue, tell me am I gettin' through?
G7
I keep hangin' on, tryin' to learn the song
C G
But I never do.
C Dm
Oh, moody blue, tell me who I'm talkin' to?
G7
You're like night and day, and it's hard to say
C
Which one is you.

Link | Dm | G ||

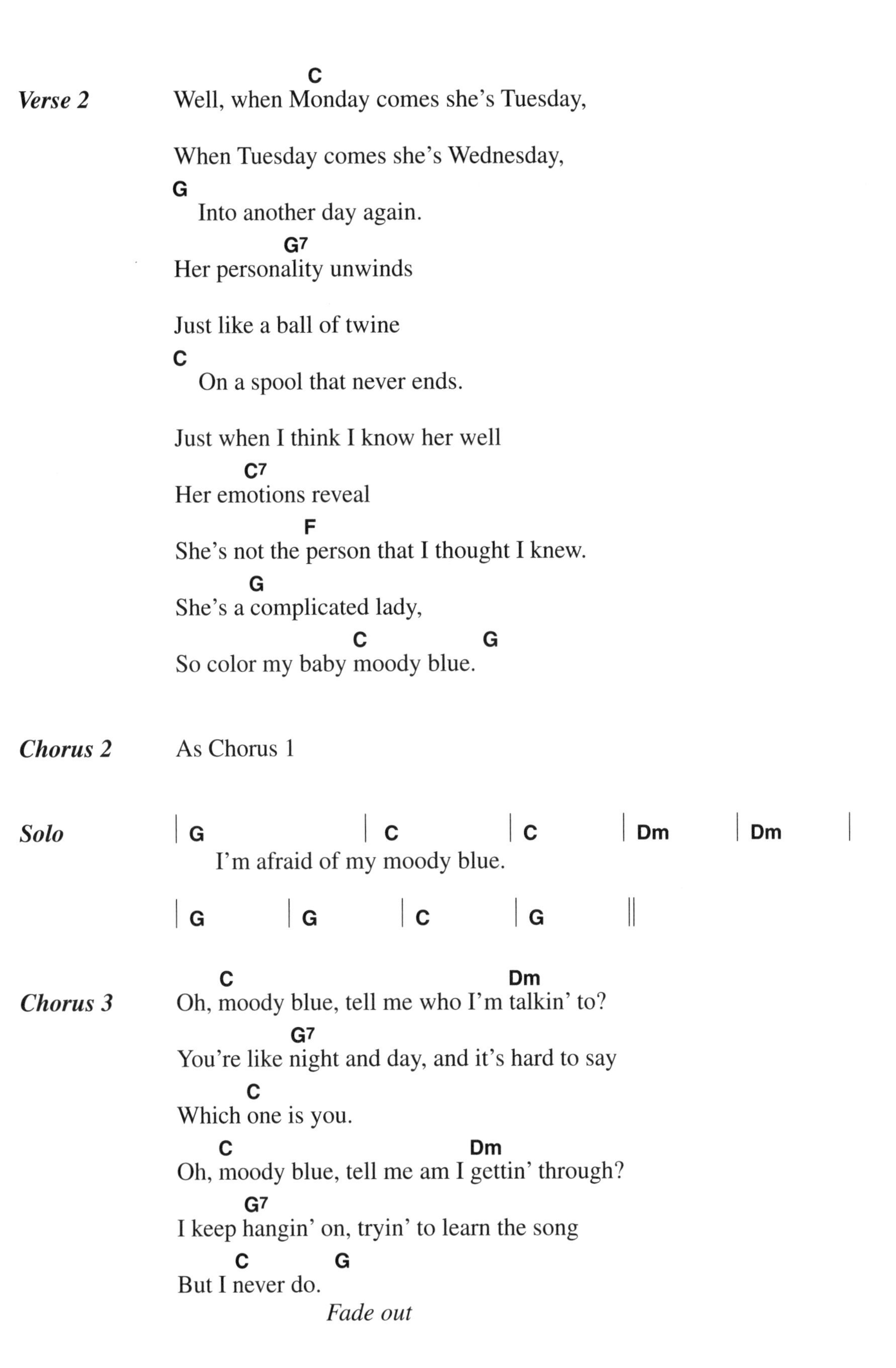

```
                         C
Verse 2      Well, when Monday comes she's Tuesday,

             When Tuesday comes she's Wednesday,
             G
               Into another day again.
                      G7
             Her personality unwinds

             Just like a ball of twine
             C
               On a spool that never ends.

             Just when I think I know her well
                  C7
             Her emotions reveal
                         F
             She's not the person that I thought I knew.
                   G
             She's a complicated lady,
                                C          G
             So color my baby moody blue.


Chorus 2     As Chorus 1


Solo         | G             | C          | C        | Dm        | Dm        |
                I'm afraid of my moody blue.

             | G        | G        | C        | G        ||


                C                      Dm
Chorus 3     Oh, moody blue, tell me who I'm talkin' to?
                       G7
             You're like night and day, and it's hard to say
                  C
             Which one is you.
                C                   Dm
             Oh, moody blue, tell me am I gettin' through?
                  G7
             I keep hangin' on, tryin' to learn the song
                 C       G
             But I never do.
                           Fade out
```

Way Down

Words & Music by
Layng Martine, Jr.

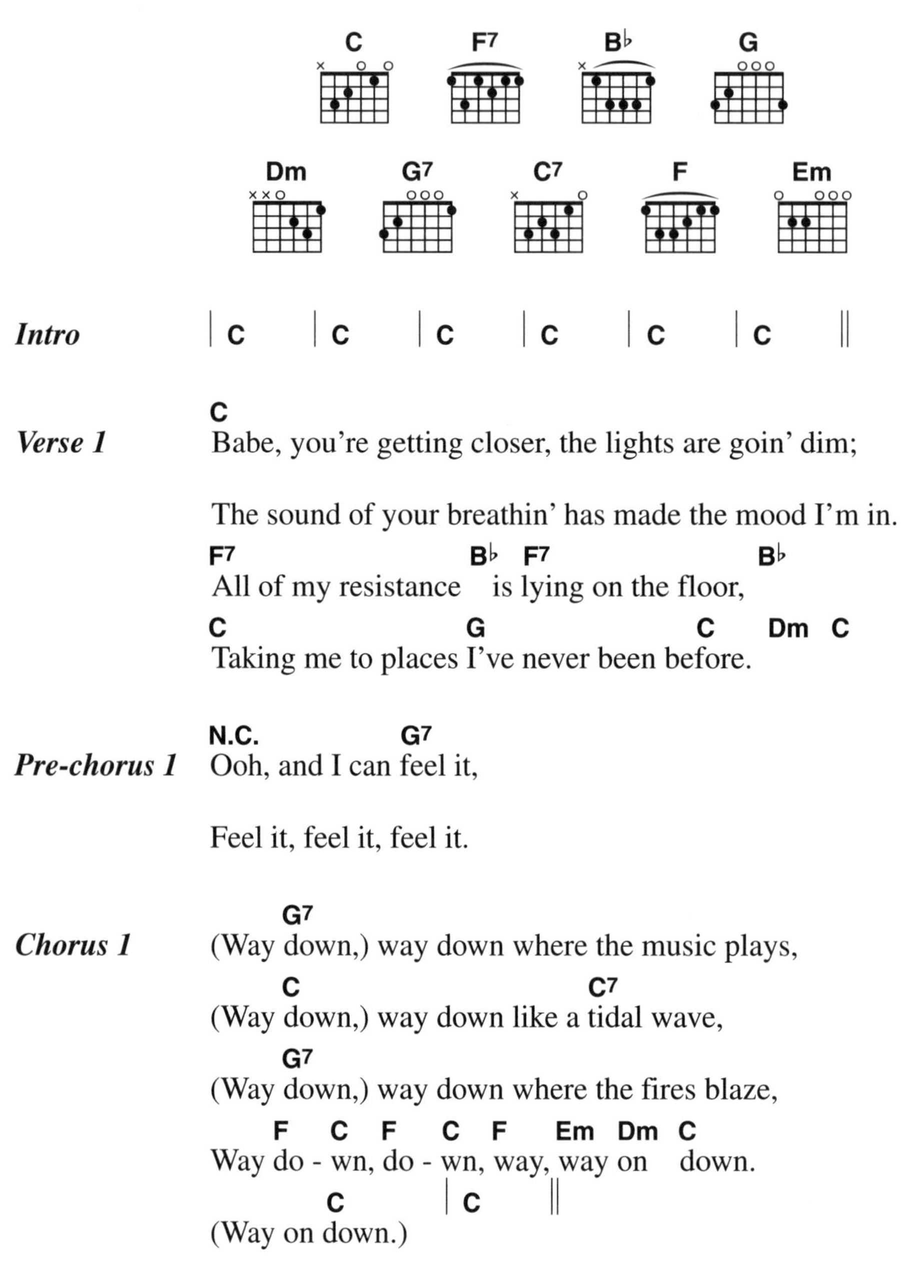

Intro | C | C | C | C | C | C ||

Verse 1

```
C
Babe, you're getting closer, the lights are goin' dim;

The sound of your breathin' has made the mood I'm in.
F7                          B♭  F7                  B♭
All of my resistance    is lying on the floor,
C                        G                   C     Dm   C
Taking me to places I've never been before.
```

Pre-chorus 1

```
N.C.                G7
Ooh, and I can feel it,

Feel it, feel it, feel it.
```

Chorus 1

```
       G7
(Way down,) way down where the music plays,
       C                        C7
(Way down,) way down like a tidal wave,
       G7
(Way down,) way down where the fires blaze,
      F    C    F     C    F      Em   Dm   C
Way do - wn, do - wn, way, way on      down.
          C          | C      ||
(Way on down.)
```

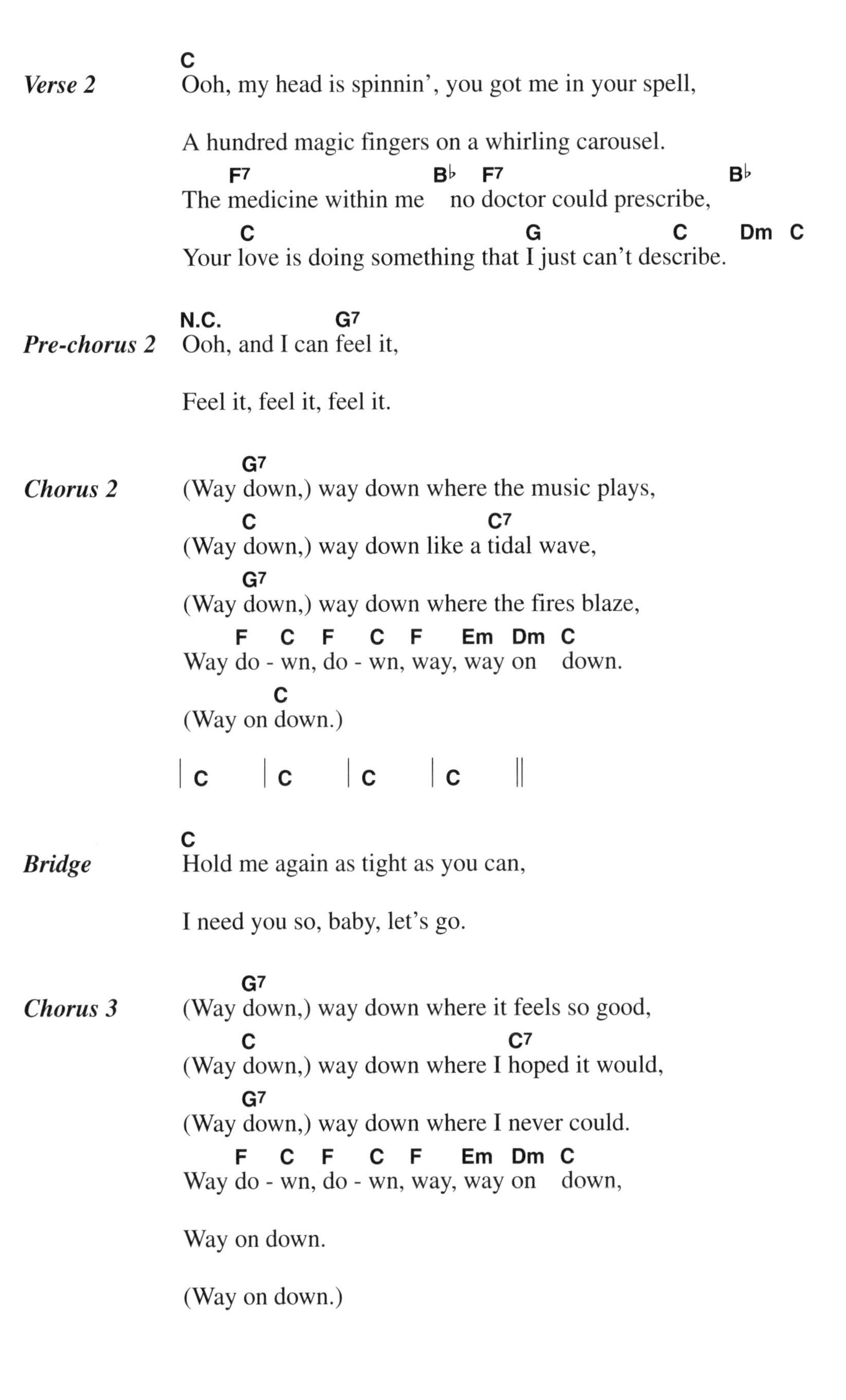
C
Verse 2 Ooh, my head is spinnin', you got me in your spell,
A hundred magic fingers on a whirling carousel.
F7 B♭ F7 B♭
The medicine within me no doctor could prescribe,
C G C Dm C
Your love is doing something that I just can't describe.
N.C. G7
Pre-chorus 2 Ooh, and I can feel it,
Feel it, feel it, feel it.
G7
Chorus 2 (Way down,) way down where the music plays,
C C7
(Way down,) way down like a tidal wave,
G7
(Way down,) way down where the fires blaze,
F C F C F Em Dm C
Way do - wn, do - wn, way, way on down.
C
(Way on down.)
| C | C | C | C ||
C
Bridge Hold me again as tight as you can,
I need you so, baby, let's go.
G7
Chorus 3 (Way down,) way down where it feels so good,
C C7
(Way down,) way down where I hoped it would,
G7
(Way down,) way down where I never could.
F C F C F Em Dm C
Way do - wn, do - wn, way, way on down,
Way on down.
(Way on down.)

I Just Can't Help Believin'

Words & Music by
Barry Mann & Cynthia Weil

Capo first fret

Intro

|: E | E6/9 | E | E6/9 :|

Verse 1

E
I just can't help believin'
Emaj7
When she smiles up soft and gentle
F♯m
With a trace of misty morning
B7 E E6/9 E E6/9
And a promise of tomorrow in her eyes.
E
I just can't help believin'
Emaj7
When she's lying close beside me
E7 A Am7
And my heart beats with the rhythm of her sighs.

Chorus 1

E E6/9 E E6/9
This time the girl is gonna stay,
E A B7sus4 B7
This time the girl is gonna stay
N.C.
For more than just a (day.)

Link 1

| E | E6/9 | E | E6/9 ||
day.

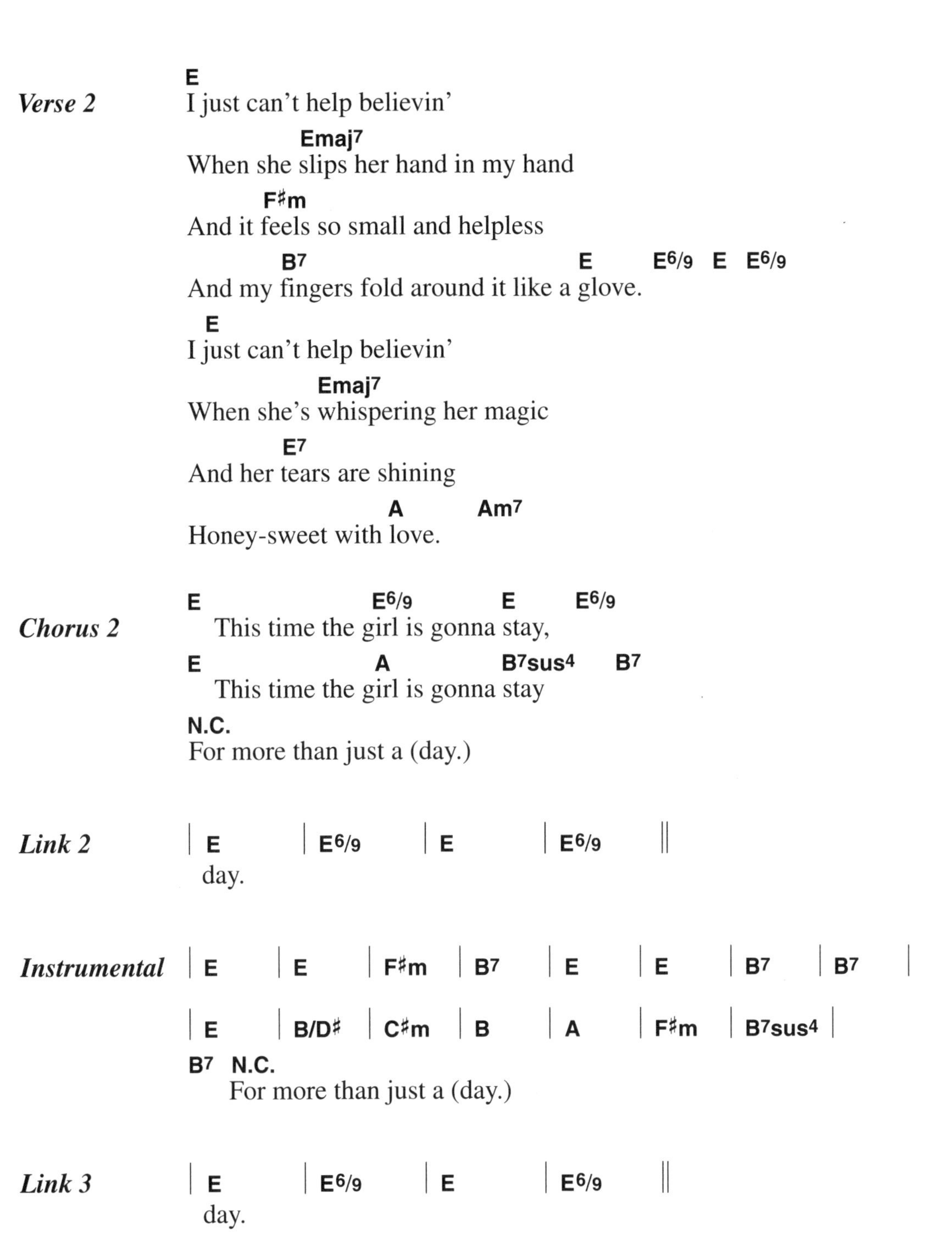
E
Verse 2 I just can't help believin'
Emaj7
When she slips her hand in my hand
F♯m
And it feels so small and helpless
B7 E E6/9 E E6/9
And my fingers fold around it like a glove.
E
I just can't help believin'
Emaj7
When she's whispering her magic
E7
And her tears are shining
A Am7
Honey-sweet with love.
E E6/9 E E6/9
Chorus 2 This time the girl is gonna stay,
E A B7sus4 B7
This time the girl is gonna stay
N.C.
For more than just a (day.)
Link 2 | E | E6/9 | E | E6/9 ||
day.
Instrumental | E | E | F♯m | B7 | E | E | B7 | B7 |
| E | B/D♯ | C♯m | B | A | F♯m | B7sus4 |
B7 N.C.
For more than just a (day.)
Link 3 | E | E6/9 | E | E6/9 ||
day.

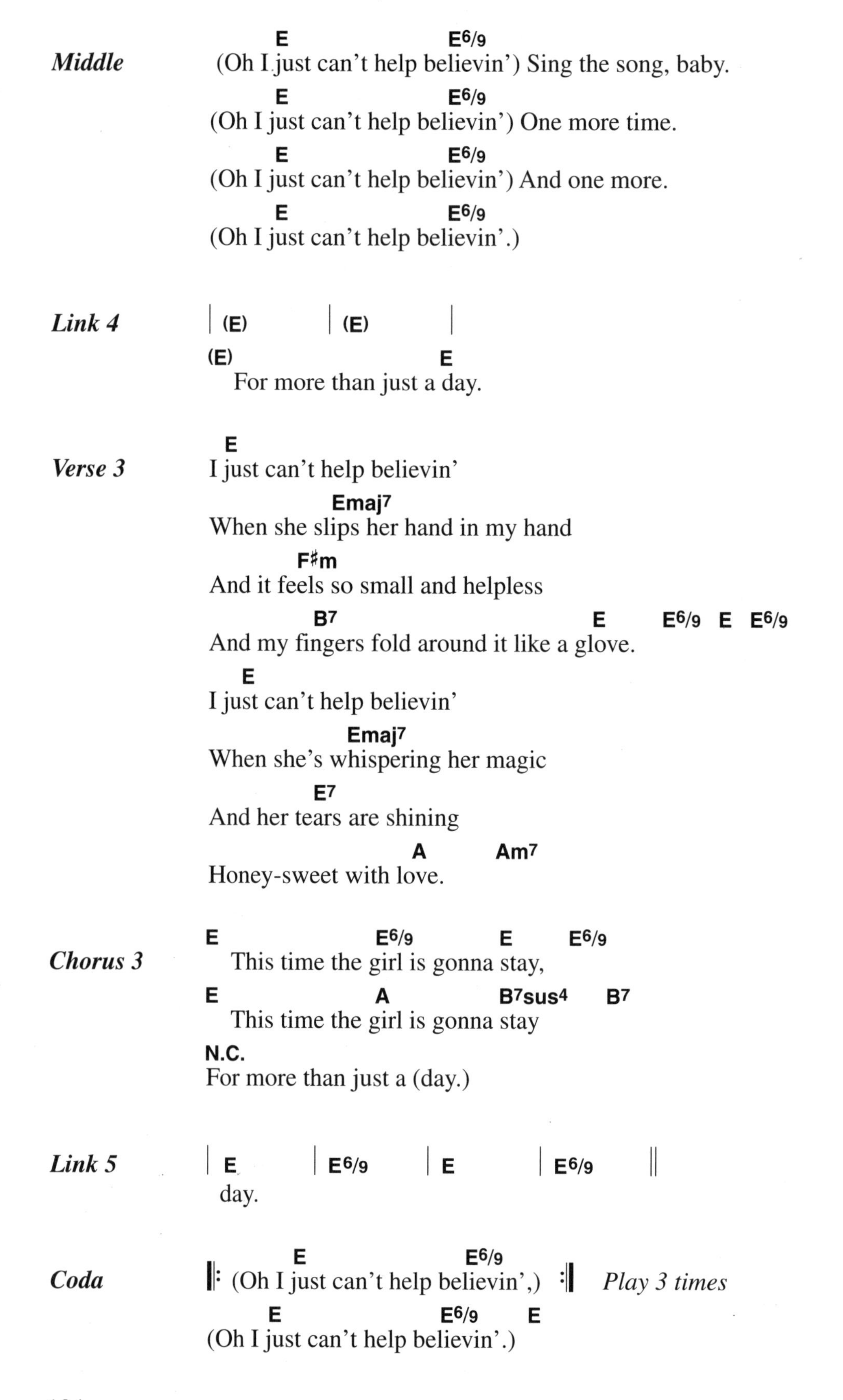

Middle

E E6/9
(Oh I just can't help believin') Sing the song, baby.

E E6/9
(Oh I just can't help believin') One more time.

E E6/9
(Oh I just can't help believin') And one more.

E E6/9
(Oh I just can't help believin'.)

Link 4

| (E) | (E) |

(E) E
For more than just a day.

Verse 3

E
I just can't help believin'

Emaj7
When she slips her hand in my hand

F♯m
And it feels so small and helpless

B7 E E6/9 E E6/9
And my fingers fold around it like a glove.

E
I just can't help believin'

Emaj7
When she's whispering her magic

E7
And her tears are shining

A Am7
Honey-sweet with love.

Chorus 3

E E6/9 E E6/9
This time the girl is gonna stay,

E A B7sus4 B7
This time the girl is gonna stay

N.C.
For more than just a (day.)

Link 5

| E | E6/9 | E | E6/9 ||
day.

Coda

E E6/9
𝄆 (Oh I just can't help believin',) 𝄇 *Play 3 times*

E E6/9 E
(Oh I just can't help believin'.)

9/08(167055)